HOW TO BE THE PERFECT LOVER

'More and more people [...]
today. But also [...]
understanding [...]
anyone who [...]
of it. They t[...]
don't tell you how to get yourself into the right
physical and emotional condition to appreciate
and enjoy what they suggest . . . The erotic senses,
besides being invisible, are capricious and difficult
to handle. What is it about a particular type of
girl, a particular type of face and figure, that
makes her sexually exciting?

There aren't any concrete answers to these questions, but this book will help you understand your
own sexual likes and dislikes to the point where
you will be able to manipulate them during your
relationships to your own – and to your lover's –
explicit advantage.'

Graham Masterton

HOW TO BE THE PERFECT LOVER

Graham Masterton

Nexus
A Star Book
Published in 1983
by the Paperback Division of
W. H. Allen & Co. PLC
26 Grand Union Centre,
338 Ladbroke Grove, London W1O 5AH
Reprinted 1991

Published by arrangement with Grove Press, Inc., New York

Printed and bound in Great Britain by
Cox & Wyman Ltd, Reading, Berks.

ISBN 0 352 31378 1

CONTENTS

Foreword

If you asked me what my definition of a "perfect lover" is, I'd say any man who is confident that he gives as good as he gets. In other words, a man who is sure that he is pleasing and stimulating his partner to the same degree that he is enjoying himself.

That's all very well, you say—but how can a man ever know that? How can he know what a girl feels when he touches her *here* or kisses her *there*? How can he know she's not *pretending* to enjoy herself, when really she wishes he would try some other position or some other technique?

The answer lies in a word that is seldom connected with sex—*training*. These days, many of us are educated into the *facts* of sex, but there is no facility at all for preparing ourselves in practical terms for what, after all, is one of the most physically and mentally strenuous activities we will ever engage in.

And when you consider the importance of sex in our intimate relationships, and the magnitude of the social and emotional problems when things do go wrong, it seems absurdly lopsided that there are infinitely better opportunities to train ourselves for engineering, swimming, or absolutely anything. There are more books about flower arranging than there are about sex, and whose marriage ever hinged on a flower arrangement?

It's true that more and more manuals on sex are available today. But almost all of these suffer from a lack of understanding of the real difficulties that face anyone who wants to be as good in bed as he is out of it. They tell you what to *do*, all right, but they don't tell you how to get yourself into the proper physical and emotional condition to appreciate and enjoy what they suggest.

It's like telling a man who has only driven a family car how to drive a racing car. Unless his body and mind are trained for it, the information is next to useless.

I have worked on publications dealing with sexual topics for eight years—I have edited *Penthouse, Mayfair, Forum,* and the Swedish pornography magazine *Private*—and written five books on sexual behavior. During this time I have developed close relationships with those rare but significant people in the world who devote most of their energies to studying, evaluating, and passing on their knowledge and understanding about sex.

From their work, and from my own, I have brought together a comprehensive plan that will enable you to develop yourselves sexually to a high level.

I have drawn on the knowledge of psychiatrists, psychologists, dieticians, physical training experts, doctors, prostitutes, sex therapists—anyone who has valuable experience and insight.

Like any training program, *How to Be the Perfect Lover* is as effective as you want to make it. Just as a slimming diet won't make any appreciable inroads on your extra weight if you're not strict about it, so the diets and exercises in this book won't develop your erotic potential unless you adhere to them fairly regularly.

Mind you, many of the exercises in the course are a good deal more pleasurable than those you'll do with Jack LaLanne. He never told anyone to masturbate five times in an hour—well, not publicly.

It is probably the mental and emotional side of sexual training that is most important, however. While the basic capabilities of the penis can be relatively easily controlled (when it's up, you can see it's up), the erotic senses, besides being invisible, are capricious and difficult to handle. Why are some men aroused by stockings and garters? Why do some men like being bitten and scratched during lovemaking, while others hate it? What is it about a particular type of girl, a particular type of face and figure, that makes her sexually exciting?

There aren't any concrete answers to these questions, but this book will help you understand your own sexual likes and dislikes to the point where you will be able to manipulate them during your relationships to your own—and to your lover's—explicit advantage. In other words, while you may not know *why* you are feeling the way you are, you will at least recognize *what* you are feeling and how best you can exploit your feelings in your lovemaking.

There's one other vital part of sexual relationships which this book—unlike so many others—does not ignore. That is how to find a lover, and how to recognize the possibilities of a sexual affair developing between you. So many readers of the magazines for which I have worked have written and telephoned me and asked simply: "Knowing all about sex is one thing, but what good is it if I haven't got a girl?"

Finding and keeping a girl is one of the most important parts of being a perfect lover, and that's why I haven't ducked the issue. It's great to be great in the sack, but you can't have intercourse with yourself (or if you can, you ought to be in the *Guinness Book of Records*).

The best sex takes place in the context of a smooth and anxiety-free relationship. Any stress or awkwardness outside the bedroom will take its toll on your performance between the sheets. That's why it is *absolutely vital* to have your non-sex life as organized as your erotic activities.

One final point—I am not a strong believer in constant self-analysis. The more you stew over a sexual problem, the harder it becomes to solve. But when you are putting into practice on a real girl the training you will acquire through this book, it will be useful for you to keep a private log on your emotional and sexual performance.

In that way, you will always have a record of the way in which you became—as you are about to become—the perfect lover.

Graham Masterton

ONE:

What Kind of Lover Are You?

Whatever kind of lover you are, you're not a *bad* lover. No man is a bad lover. Some are impatient, clumsy, or ignorant. Some are trying to have a successful sex relationship with a girl who is not, and never will be, their type.

But they are *trying,* and nobody who tries to make love well can be a bad lover.

The trouble is, it's hard to admit your own faults, particularly in an area where our masculine pride is so sensitive. It's a staple ingredient in your self-respect as a man that you should believe you are good in bed.

Not just *think* it or *guess* it—but *believe* it.

Until you can admit your shortcomings, you can never satisfactorily improve your style and technique. But the main point to bear in mind is that whatever your problems, *you are capable of becoming a truly memorable lover*—the kind of man a girl will never really forget all her life.

The hardest part of analyzing your sexual weak spots is that, quite often, you won't even know you have them. And you won't get any help from your wife or girl friend, either. Women are not in the habit of criticizing a man's sexual ability, particularly if they love him, and a lot of the time they don't even know what's wrong themselves.

It is vital, however, to understand your erotic difficulties before you can train yourself out of them. Any training scheme, if it's going to work, has got to hit right at your worst points, and help you to strengthen them. In other words, it's no good having the world's most perfectly developed biceps if you've still got the world's most scrawnily underdeveloped chest.

Some sexual problems are easier to nail down than others. Do you come too soon, for instance—or do you sometimes find that you can't come at all? Does your penis collapse on you at the crucial moment? Do you find yourself confused by your girl friend's vaginal geography? Can you bring your girl friend to orgasm or not?

But other problems are a little trickier. Do you find it hard to concentrate mentally when you're making love? Do you find it difficult to decide what position to use? Do you finish lovemaking feeling dissatisfied without knowing why?

The first thing to remember, though, whether your problems are clear-cut or confused, is that you're by no means the only man who has them, and that they can mostly be overcome.

Here's a very common difficulty that was described to me by a Chicago businessman in a letter to one of my magazines:

"I made a mistake when I was very young, only twenty-one, and married a girl I didn't really love at all. I guess I just was infatuated with her, and infatuated with the idea of being a husband. After six years of marriage, I met Lucia, a very attractive and vivacious girl, at a computer conference, and got to know her pretty well on a business level.

"One evening I asked Lucia out to dinner, and one thing led to another. In the cab back to her apartment, I kissed her, and it was like all the lights in New York going on at once. In the elevator, we kissed some more, and I started fondling her breasts through her blouse, and by the time we unlocked the door and got into the place, we were both panting for it like dogs.

"We literally hurled our clothes off and got on to the bed. She opened up her legs for me immediately, and she was wet and shivering and all ready to go. And then came the great disaster. I slid my prick into her, and before I knew what had happened I had shot my load.

"She was very good about it. Even though she was disappointed, she took it as a compliment that I was so worked up about her, and she did a great deal to reassure me. We fixed up another date when we both knew we'd have more time to make love.

"The next time, everything was much cooler and smoother. We had a quiet meal in her apartment, had a few drinks to soothe ourselves down, and then went into the bathroom to share a bath together.

"We were sitting in the bathtub, and I had a real hard erection, feeling her all slippery and naked. She held my prick gently in her hand, and bent forward, and just closed her mouth around the end of it, which was all that was showing out of the water. The next thing I knew, I came straight into her mouth. Again, she didn't mind. She was a sophisticated girl, and she didn't mind me coming in her mouth. I think she felt a sort of triumph, in a way, and she sat there smiling with my come all down her chin.

"But to me, it was a real blow. I couldn't get another hard-on that evening, so that was it. I had gone over for a screw, and ended up with little more than a wash.

"It never got any better. Every time I tried to have sex with Lucia, I shot the whole works before anything had happened. The strange thing is, it had never happened with my wife, and it still doesn't happen with her. I have better sex with the woman I don't love than I do with the woman I do love."

Ejaculatio praecox—premature ejaculation—is the single most widespread male sexual problem after impotence. It happens to boys of fourteen and it happens to men of fifty. The man who wrote the account you've just read was twenty-nine, but he could just as easily have been twenty years older.

Later on in this book, we'll go much more deeply into premature ejaculation and see what kind of training can help a man to get over it. But at the moment, as we try and build up a picture of what kind of lovers we are, I've used this true personal account just to show that no sexual problem is a simple one.

There's no such thing as purely animal sex. There are times when you feel pretty animal about it, and leap around the bed like orangutans in the mosquito season, but your intellect is never totally switched off.

Your cock is completely linked up to your brain. If your gray matter gets excited, then your cock does. If there's something a little bit amiss up there, then your cock's performance can suffer.

Here's another very typical sexual situation—this time from a young Englishman of twenty-five:

"I have to admit that I have only once been to bed with a girl that I really liked. I am not a particularly unattractive-looking person, but I always seem to be the one who ends up with the ugliest girl friends. I know that, whatever friend I go out with, if there are two girls to be picked up, I will invariably get the one with the thick-rimmed glasses or the frizzy hair.

"The one girl that I really liked—and she was terribly pretty—was a girl I met when I went on holiday to Spain at the age of nineteen. I fell in love with her almost at first sight, and I think the sun and the wine and everything else made it easier for me to be relaxed and confident with her. I made up my mind that I wasn't going to make a mess of this relationship, like I always seemed to before.

"Her name was Alison. She had short dark hair, big blue eyes, and a fantastic figure. She was the sort of girl that made everybody's head turn when she walked into a room, and I found that really intoxicating, because I had never been out with a girl like that before.

"I can remember the night we first made love. We'd been swimming in the afternoon and we were both very tired, and she came back to my hotel room for a beer. We lay side by side on the bed and talked for a while, and then we started kissing. She only had her bikini on, and a sort of beach wrap around her shoulders. I got her bikini top undone, it was easier than a bra, and her nipples went tremendously stiff. I couldn't hide the way I was feeling by then, because I only had swimming trunks on as well. I put my hand in her bikini pants, and got them off, and then we made love. I think I was probably a little bit clumsy, but we both enjoyed it, and I think I satisfied her.

"After that, I fell for her so much you wouldn't believe it. I didn't want to be away from her. But then she started making sarcastic comments to me, and complaining that I followed her around. She got sulkier, and the more I tried to do the things she wanted me to do, the sulkier she seemed to get. About two or three days later, I saw her on the beach with a Spanish guy. They were kissing and laughing and carrying on just the way she and I had been only a few days before. It's been a long time since that happened, but I haven't forgotten it, and I haven't forgotten her. If she was back with me now, I'd give her anything she wanted."

This is more of a love problem than a sex problem— but again it is a very common hangup, and it shows that even though you can be the best performer in the universe once you get a girl into bed, you've got to get her there first—and keep her there. The things that go wrong with your sex life and the things that are right with your sex life are matters of both *mind* and *body*.

That's why this chapter has to do some emotional plumbing as well as some physical assessment. Sex is a little like kung fu—your thoughts and your actions have to work together with one well-oiled accord. The only difference is, with kung fu you make fewer friends.

Here's a problem that seems to be just a sex problem, but on closer examination has just those same ingredients of thought and deed. It was sent to me by an American engineer, aged thirty-six:

"This might sound like kind of an odd question, but can you please explain to me exactly where a woman's clitoris is, what it does, and how I can properly manipulate it?

"I am unmarried, although I have been engaged once, and I guess I have a reasonable number of escorts. But to tell the God's honest truth, I have only a few times been able to make a woman come to her orgasm, and on those few occasions I haven't been sure myself what I've done.

"I've read books on sex, and I know that the clitoris is kind of the seat of a woman's sexual feelings, but a woman's actual vagina is very different from a drawing when you're there in the sack with her. I've tried to find it with my fingers and with one or two girls I've even managed to have a pretty close look, but it all seems like a lot of complicated flesh to me.

"I once went to bed with a girl I met in Detroit, in a bar. I didn't manage to get her to an orgasm, and afterward she was so heated up about it that she asked me to masturbate her. I tried to, but my efforts only made matters worse. She said I was hurting her and making her feel uncomfortable, so I gave up, much to my embarrassment.

"All I want, in clear specific detail, is a description of how to locate the clitoris easily, and what exact manipulations to perform on it once I've found it."

As with other problems I've quoted here we'll go into the fleshy details of how to track down the elusive clitoris in a later chapter. But notice the *emotional* reservations that this man has. He has never felt able to ask a girl for help in stimulating her. He feels that, as a man, he ought to know—even though he doesn't—and that girls *expect* him to know. He simply can't communicate with the girls he sleeps with, even though he is involved with them in the most intimate act that two people can perform together.

Not so easy, is it?

For one final example of how closely mind and penis are linked, here's part of a letter I received from another American, a sales executive, aged thirty-two:

"Even though I say it myself, I am a terrific stud. I have always been a horny sort of a guy, with a healthy interest in the opposite sex, and I have read *Playboy* and stag books and what have you from college.

"I was lucky enough to meet a girl who shared my interest in sex, and we spent a lot of time balling. She's a cute girl, but she's more than that, she's a Vassar graduate, and is destined for big things in the world of academe.

"To begin with, we got on together terrifically. I never asked her about her books and she never asked me about my sales. What we had in common was a big interest in fucking. She used to come around to my place in the evening, when we'd both finished work, and a lot of the time she'd already taken off her panties on the way, and the first thing I'd do is put my hand up her little skirt and feel her pussy all juiced up and ready to roll.

"Why she went for me was because, even though I'm just a regular joe with straightforward interests, I look good, I drive a Mark IV Lincoln Continental, and I fuck like Tarzan. If those qualifications aren't good enough for any girl, I'd like to know what qualifications are.

"But we've been having more and more problems

lately. She's been getting less and less interested in fucking, and the less she's interested in fucking, the more I want to make her fuck. Some evenings, it's been almost like rape. She came around the other night and said she was just going to have some coffee and then split. While she was standing at the stove, I came up behind her with my dick right out, lifted her skirt and shoved my dick up into her—I mean it pushed her panties up inside her as well.

"She was angry about that, but at the same time she's still a sexy girl, and it ended up with us having an argument and then s.a.u.—screwing as usual. But what I want to know is, how much does she want from me? What does she want that I can't give her? Incidentally my wang when erect is seven inches exactly."

It's not difficult to see what emotional and physical problems this man faces. But what can he do about them? And what can *you* do about your own sexual shortcomings—especially if they're a lot more subtle?

For starters you need a profile of your sexual personality. Armed with this information, you can use the training in this book to its maximum advantage—picking out those chapters that are most relevant to you.

Go through the questions I've laid out on the following pages, and answer them as honestly as you can. They will help you to analyze your performance and your attitudes, and give you a fairly basic picture of your sexual qualities and potential.

Don't worry if you think you're not making a good showing with your answers. Every problem in this questionnaire can be solved by practice and training—and if you don't recognize where your difficulties lie *right now,* it will make it harder for you to overcome them.

The questionnaire is divided into two parts—emotional and physical—to make it easier for you to appreciate what training you require. But don't forget that both body and mind are completely interdependent in all your performances in bed, and that one can't operate effectively without the other.

EMOTIONS

1. Girls respect you more if you're not too familiar with them. YES/NO
2. Sex without love is not very satisfactory. AGREE/ DISAGREE
3. Virginity is a girl's most valuable possession. YES/ NO
4. I feel nervous with the opposite sex. YES/NO
5. Sometimes the woman should be sexually aggressive. YES/NO
6. I often wish that women would be more aggressive sexually. YES/NO
7. I get excited sexually very easily. YES/NO
8. I worry a lot about sex. YES/NO
9. I didn't learn the facts of life until I was quite old. YES/NO
10. Sex thoughts drive me almost crazy. YES/NO
11. It is better not to have sexual relations until you're married. YES/NO
12. My conscience bothers me too much. YES/NO
13. Sex should not be used for personal pleasure, only for reproduction. YES/NO

14. I prefer to have intercourse under the bedclothes, with the lights off. YES/NO

15. I would enjoy watching my usual partner having sex with someone else. YES/NO

16. There are some things I do only to please my sex partner. YES/NO

17. I am afraid of sexual relationships. YES/NO

18. I feel sexually less competent than my friends. YES/NO

19. I find it easy to tell my love partner what I like or dislike about her lovemaking. YES/NO

20. Physical sex is the most important part of a relationship. YES/NO

Give yourself one point whenever your answers agree with the answers given here—give yourself zero when they disagree.

1. No; 2. Disagree; 3. No; 4. No; 5. Yes; 6. Yes; 7. Yes; 8. No; 9. No; 10. Yes; 11. No; 12. No; 13. No; 14. No; 15. Yes; 16. No; 17. No; 18. No; 19. Yes; 20. Yes.

Now add up your score. If you have 14 points, your sexuality is about average.

If you have more, you are more sexually oriented than most men, and you do not need very much training in sexual arousal. If you've scored less, you can certainly benefit from the sections in this book which deal with erotic thought and sexual confidence.

Now let's turn to the physical side of your sexual personality.

PHYSICAL

1. I find it easy to get an erection. YES/NO
2. Sometimes I feel so aroused that I need immediate relief. YES/NO
3. I can only manage to make love once a day. YES/NO
4. I do not produce very much semen (average is about a teaspoonful). YES/NO
5. There are times during lovemaking when my erection subsides. YES/NO
6. I am irritated when my love partner caresses my anus. YES/NO
7. There are many times when I find it difficult to reach a climax. YES/NO
8. After making love, I feel physically exhausted. YES/NO
9. I can achieve a new erection less than half an hour after having reached a climax. YES/NO
10. Sometimes, even when my partner stimulates me, I cannot get an erection. YES/NO
11. If I do not have sex for a week, I have wet dreams (emission of semen during sleep). YES/NO
12. I usually want to go to sleep after making love. YES/NO
13. My partner can bring me to a climax by fellatio (caressing the penis with the mouth). YES/NO
14. Sometimes I feel very little sensation in my penis during sex. YES/NO
15. I ejaculate very quickly after putting my penis into my love partner. YES/NO

16. Sometimes I can only reach a climax in certain sexual positions.   YES/NO
17. I really prefer the climax I reach through masturbation to the climax I have during coitus.   YES/NO
18. I cannot perform after a few drinks.   YES/NO
19. My penis never seems to get quite hard enough. YES/NO
20. I can easily control the moment of ejaculation. YES/NO

As in the questions for emotion, give yourself one point when your answer agrees with the following answers, and nothing if it disagrees.

1. Yes; 2. Yes; 3. No; 4. No; 5. No; 6. No; 7. No; 8. No; 9. Yes; 10. No; 11. Yes; 12. No; 13. Yes; 14. No; 15. No; 16. No; 17. No; 18. No; 19. No; 20. Yes.

If you scored around 16, you're an average man in reasonable sexual condition. More, and you haven't got a lot to worry about when it comes to a straightforward sexual performance. Less—well, you need a little more training to reach the point of becoming a perfect lover.

I'd like to point out that these questionnaires are just to help you draw a profile of your sexual attitudes and potential, and that there is absolutely no need to get anxious if your score is drastically different from the averages given here. All of us are very different in our emotional and physical makeup, and there's no reason why you can't be happy with a double zero for both quizzes—or a double 20 for that matter.

All these questions can do is give you a picture of yourself that will assist you to bring yourself up to that blessed state of perfect lovership.

HOW TO BE THE PERFECT LOVER

Right now, for those of you who found your ratings a little droopy in the physical section (and for everyone else who's interested in developing a few vital talents), here's the first piece of good hard training for that very sensitive part of you.

TWO:

Ask Not What Your Erection Can Do for You

There it is, squidged up between your legs as you're sitting there reading this—man's greatest sexual asset and also his heaviest sexual hangup. His penis.

The first thing that men worry about is whether their penis is big enough. The answer that almost every sex book I've ever read gives is: "Of course it's big enough." "It's not the size that counts—it's what you do with it," and probably the most fatuous comment of all, in *The Sensuous Man* by "M" or "Z" or whoever it was: "It reaches your body, doesn't it?"

I hate to shatter the rosy illusion that it doesn't matter whether you have a big cock or a small cock, but the simple truth is that it *does*. It matters to you and it matters to the girls you make love to. Even though the actual discrepancies in size between what is classed as a "below-average" penis and what is classed as an "above-average" penis are minimal, they can be enough to make a difference that you—and she—can feel.

The fairly average worldwide penis is around six inches long, when erect. For some strange physiological reason, there is less variance in size between erect penises than there is between floppy penises. (I call them floppy because I can't stand the word *flaccid*.) That means that men with *small* floppy penises grow in size when they get a hard-on proportionately more than men with *large* floppy penises. Size when standing at ease is therefore nothing to go by.

You can see from erotic literature, though, that a large penis is more sexually exciting—in the same way that large breasts can be. All this business about "I felt he was going to split me open with his massive dick" does a lot for the aggressive male ego, and a lot for the passive female personality.

Berth Milton, the photographer/editor of the Swedish magazine *Private,* for which I worked for some time, once produced a sequence of pictures about a Stone Age girl called Lopa, who gets graphically raped by a Stone Age man called Juri. I showed this pictorial story to more than a dozen women, and they all agreed that it was extremely erotic—particularly the scenes where Juri's huge erection forced its way into the struggling Lopa. The women actually relished the idea of being pried open by a cock that seemed too large for them to take.

Now if you think your penis is smaller than average, or you've just got out your ruler and found that it really is, you may be thinking from what I've just said that you're at an intolerable sexual disadvantage.

Well, of course, you're not. You're mature enough and sensible enough to recognize that you weren't the one who chose your penis. Happily there are plenty of techniques you can use in which it is actually better to have a smaller penis than a larger one.

This is just the kind of sexual attitude I believe to be so important. It is no good glossing over emotional and physical differences and problems. In fact, it is criminal to pretend that we're all just as good as each other when it comes to sex, because we know damn well we're not, and no amount of consolation is going to make us feel any better about it. What we've got to do is recognize our problems and do something positive about them.

While we're talking about penis size, it's worth mentioning that there are several so-called penis developers on the market. The most common is a vacuum tube into which you insert your cock, thereby causing it to swell above its natural size. There's no doubt that while it's in the tube, your penis looks impressively large. Once you take it out of the vacuum, however, it tends to go back to the size it was before. So, unless you're prepared to walk around with a vacuum pump on the end of your cock, it's probably better to accept it as it is.

Robert Chartham, with whom I worked on *Forum* magazine for some time, claims that the developer he tried did him a little bit of good sizewise, and I wouldn't dispute that. All I would say is that his extra tidbit undoubtedly didn't do much for his sexual performance, one way or the other. You can buy developers if you like, but I think they're a waste of money.

No, stick with what you've got. And if you follow the special techniques for small penises which I've included in this book, you should never worry about it again—and never need spurious reassurance about it either.

No, I'm not telling you how big mine is.

There's another trouble with penises, apart from the fact that they're not all the same size. For satisfactory sexual intercourse (notice I didn't say for satisfactory *sex*) they have to be more or less erect, and the erecter the better.

Unfortunately, all kinds of things affect the penis's ability to fill itself with blood to the point where it is hard enough to slide its way into a woman's vagina.

We needn't get too involved with the completely controllable external factors which sometimes cause the penis to be limp when it should be stiff. You already know what alcohol does to an erection (brewer's droop), or excessive tiredness or illness or drugs. The way to avoid these little difficulties is not to drink too much, stay in bed on Sunday mornings, avoid children with obvious measle spots, and smoke less marijuana. It may mean less fun in your life, but what's a little abstinence compared with an erection like the Empire State Building.

But there are times when you want and perhaps need to make love and find that some of these external factors are handicapping your erection. When you drank those first eight whiskies, perhaps you didn't know that five minutes later, a tempting brunette would come your way. What do you do then?

Black coffee and benzedrine is one answer, but it's not infallible. All you can really do is ride your temporary embarrassment out, and hope that the woman is woman enough to understand. Remember that you *cannot help it*, and it is no reflection on your normal state of virility.

Explain your problem without apology and without remorse, and make a date for tomorrow. You stand more chance of winning out this way than by struggling on and on and on to get your disobedient penis to rise. You're not an Indian snake charmer, you're a normal imperfect man.

There's another reason why your penis won't go up, and it's much more complex and intractable.

It's called *anxiety*.

Anxiety about almost anything can kill the healthiest erection. You might be anxious about the implications of the sexual relationship you're involved in at the very moment (particularly if you're married to someone else). You could be anxious about money, about your job, or whether your car needs a 6,000-mile check-up.

One of the greatest anxieties of all, according to Professor Hans Eysenck at London's Maudsley Institute, with whom I discussed this particular subject, is anxiety about whether your penis is actually going to stiffen.

This anxiety causes it to flop, and next time you try to get it up you're anxious because your anxiety caused it to flop. And so on, and so on and, unless you get some help, so on. . . .

A lot of the exercises in this book will help you to discipline your mind to blot out minor worries, like financial and job anxieties. I'm not saying it's easy, but it can be done.

But what about the downward spiral of anxiety about the erection itself?

Drs. Phyllis and Eberhard Kronhausen, the world-famous man-and-wife team of clinical psychologists and sexologists, put the whole problem in very neat perspective. They said they believed implicitly not only in a man's right to succeed in bed, but in his *right to fail*.

This is probably the first time you've read a book about sex which has told you that it's all right if you can't get a hard-on. But actually it is all right, provided you don't panic and rush for the fire exit.

The thing to do is to forget about yourself and whether you can get it up or not, and concentrate *entirely* on giving the woman a good time. It's a great challenge, in actual fact. Can you bring her to orgasm, giving her the maximum amount of pleasure, completely without the aid of your penis? Use your fingers, as I'll show you how to later in this book, and your tongue, as I'll also demonstrate later.

If you masturbate her and "cunniling" her well enough, you'll complete her satisfaction and pleasure, and also do a great deal to restore your own confidence in yourself as a lover. You may also find that once you stop worrying about whether your cock will go up or not, it will impertinently oblige with an erection. Sexual arousal is infectious, and the things that you do to your partner could bring you to the boil.

But *don't* be dejected if you achieve an erection, and then as soon as you start trying to do something with it, it collapses on you. You will feel both mad and frustrated, but an outburst of anger or self-pity will demolish all the respect you've been painstakingly building up with your tongue and your fingers. Laugh it off (you're allowed a hollow laugh). If she's understanding enough to make love to, she's understanding enough to realize that you can't invent the hydrogen bomb every day.

It's worth trying the same technique if you're affected by alcohol or indigestion or aspirin. You can only do what you can do, after all, and there is nothing more impossible than a penis that refuses to do its stuff. As one stage comedian remarked, "It's like trying to shove two pounds of melted butter up a wildcat's ass with a red-hot screwdriver."

Your cock is more likely to do what it's told, however, if it's properly trained and cared for.

Considering how complex and wondrous and sensitive and all the rest your male organ is, you treat it with marked contempt. It spends all day crushed up between your thighs, only whipped out for the occasional quick pee, and after all that, it's expected to emerge, proudly standing at attention to give you one of the most noble and exquisite physical pleasures there is. Then once it's done its job, it's crammed back into your pants again for the next time.

Did Wyatt Earp treat his Buntline Special like that? Of course not. He only shot straight because he looked after his equipment.

Start looking at your penis in a different way. Take your trousers and underpants off, go to the mirror, and examine just what it is you've got there. It's mobile, sensitive, and really very delicate. It can respond not only to physical touch, but to erotic thoughts as well. You can think yourself into an erection.

Exercise One:
Stand naked in front of the mirror, and try to *think* your cock into erection. Think of the most erotic fantasies you can. Think of girls sucking and fondling your penis, think of girls lying in front of you with their legs widespread. Think of a girl you particularly want, and imagine lying in bed with her, about to slide yourself into her. Think what you like, but without touching yourself, get that penis erect.

Once you have been able to achieve erection by thought alone in this way, you are one step along the road to appreciating just how closely your sexual organ and your brain are interlinked. Try Exercise One every morning when you get up and every evening when you go to bed, every day of the week. After four of five days, you should find it easier to get your cock to stand up on command alone.

As you begin to develop mental power over your penis,

you will find you can tune your erotic sensations like an FM radio. Now comes the most difficult of exercises, but one that, in terms of building up your sexual proficiency, can be tremendously rewarding.

Exercise Two:

Lie naked in bed, and attempt to bring yourself to a climax without actually touching your penis. The first few times, you may find you have to abstain for a day or two before you can manage to ejaculate, and in the early stages, a little manual help is permissible—a few gentle strokes on the tip of your penis with your fingertips, or a firm but motionless grip on the shaft of the cock while you are thinking yourself to the point of orgasm.

This exercise requires tremendous patience and concentration, and you mustn't be discouraged if it takes you a long time to reach just one ejaculation. But even if you can only manage to arouse yourself to a pretty high level of horniness, that can still be considered a successful commission of the exercise.

While you are carrying out these exercises, start treating your penis with a little more respect.

Buy yourself, if you haven't got them already, some very brief but very supporting underpants. *Brief* to keep you cool and make you feel sexier, and *supporting* so that you can arrange your genitals in a tidy and comfortable way, and walk around all day without them walloping around inside your trousers. Don't buy underpants or trousers that are *too* tight, because there is some evidence to suggest that restricting the balls to that extent can reduce virility.

And we wouldn't want that to happen, right?

Next, buy yourself some mild and *non*astringent skin lotion. Every other evening, lie back and massage your penis with it. If you find you get turned on—even to the point of coming to a climax—don't worry about it. It shows you're a normal man, responding normally to the stimulus of having his cock rubbed.

After two or three weeks of Exercise One, give yourself a test of your sexual stamina. In other words, see how soon you can bring yourself to erection *after* you've had a climax.

I once had a letter from a Boston executive who said he had been able to train himself to get back to a state of stiffness ten minutes after each climax, and have three such erections within an hour. Now, it's not really necessary for even a perfect lover to be able to perform such feats, but *if* you're able to turn around to a woman whom you have just satisfied with yet *another* massive erection, it's so good for her ego, your ego, and both of your morales. I don't know what it does to your morals, but we'll go into that later.

Exercise Three:

Masturbate as often as you can within the space of one hour. You can use stimulating material like girlie magazines or pinups to assist you. You can even use a girl friend or wife to assist you. Aim for five times within an hour. Do this exercise once every three days only—even Casanovas are rarely called on to perform five times a day, every day.

While you're doing this exercise, try and find out whether there is any special kind of stimulus that makes you return to a state of erection more quickly. A friend of mine who tried out Exercise Three for me said that he could bring himself quite quickly back to erection by having his wife fondle his ass. He had never realized before what erotic sensations he was capable of feeling around his buttocks and anus, and now that his wife had discovered his trigger spot, she was getting far better sexual performances out of him.

Don't think, though, that when you've found a trigger spot or technique, it's *always* going to work. A great many women have complained to me that they can't arouse their husbands very easily any more—"even though I've done all the things I know he likes."

Erotic sensation is very dependent on *surprise* and *novelty,* and after a while the same techniques, no matter how exciting they were the first time they were tried, simply cease to have the same sexual value.

Some men find that they can return more quickly to a state of erection after their climax by deliberately cutting short their first ejaculation. Even though the first spurts of semen are entirely involuntary, the third and fourth and later spasms can be suppressed by physical and mental control. I don't particularly recommend this technique during lovemaking, because it does destroy the spontaneity and full enjoyment of the ejaculation, but it is worth using when you are by yourself as an exercise in mental mastery over your penis.

The thing to remember is that your penis, amazing though it is, needs control and help if it's going to perform in the best way possible. It's like a pet dog that you can train to go and fetch the morning paper for you. It will only bring back the goodies if it's fit, disciplined, and educated to obey your commands.

Here's a letter I had from one of my magazine readers about what he could do with his cock:

"At the age of twenty-three I have discovered I am capable of what I can only describe as flexing my penis. By my voluntary contraction of certain muscles in my groin, I am able to make my erect penis bob up and down.

"Shortly after this discovery I attempted lifting various small weights which I suspended from the end of my penis. I now find myself capable of lifting a one-pound weight with ease. All this work has produced an interesting by-product. I find I am now capable of producing an erection any time I choose by continually contracting these muscles."

I am not suggesting you should attempt to emulate this young man's achievements, but you could certainly try to discover which muscles you are capable of flexing and develop them to give your penis a little bit of extra twitch.

Now we've given the penis a quick rundown, let's turn to the knotty problem of how to find somewhere to put it.

THREE:

The Perfect Lover on the Prowl

It is quite obvious that, no matter how perfect a lover you are, your talents will be completely wasted if you haven't got a woman to practice them on. It's like a painter without canvas, or a car salesman with no customers.

Assuming that you haven't already got a girl friend or wife, how do you go about exercising your developing ability?

Picking up girls is comparatively easy. What's difficult is picking up the *right* girls—the girls that you both desire and respect, and who in turn both desire and respect you.

Before you even walk out of the door on your hunt for the woman you want, make sure that you feel good in yourself. Are you happy about the way you feel in your clothes? Are you happy about your hair, your grooming, the way you smell?

Remember that *confidence* is the all-important asset in successful girl-catching, and that no one can feel confident if they suddenly feel their shirt is coming out of their trousers, or that everyone is staring at their pale blue socks under black trousers.

Invest a little money in yourself, and it will do wonders for your self-esteem. Have your hair washed and trimmed at an expensive barbershop. Cut and clean your nails. Buy yourself a couple of new outfits—a good semi-formal suit and well-fitting casual outfit. Make sure your shoes are always well repaired and polished.

Top everything off with an alluring aftershave. Avoid the more obvious brands, and go for some of the more sophisticated scents—Paco Rabanne, Christian Dior, Equipage by Hermes, Signoricci. Use a deodorant at all times, and make sure that before you go out, you have a good shower or bath. I'm not suggesting you're dirty—all I'm saying is that it will give you that extra little bit of confidence.

If you have a car, for God's sake clean it. Outside and inside. There is nothing worse than climbing into someone's car and finding an ashtray overflowing, old boots and newspapers on the floor, and a general smell of oil and mildew. And while we're on the subject of cars, don't, when you're with a woman, drive like a maniac. Women have very little appreciation of the joys of racing. All they know is that they are sitting in the passenger seat and they feel scared. Be calm, smooth, confident, and drive like the gentleman you're supposed to be.

Okay—you and your car are beautiful and shining, and you're ready to go. But where?

A favorite haunt of mine in England was the college dance. If there's a college or a university near you, take the trouble to find out when they're holding functions, and check it out.

The situation is pretty similar in the United States and Europe. College towns are bursting with young women full of the joys of newfound independence, and if you're a little older and a little smoother and a little more sophisticated than most of the men they come into contact with, you're in there with a fighting chance.

If you're looking for women in a slightly more mature league, try discotheques, bars, hotels, and even airports. Take reasonable precautions, though, in places where girls normally go with an escort. The eight-foot boyfriend of that ravishing young blonde might just have stepped out for a pee, or to practice karate on a few stray bricks in the parking lot. If you've begun to move in on some girl and the grim-faced steady returns, just retire gracefully and smile all the way. They don't often hit you when you're smiling.

There are some escorts who are obviously no problem, however; these include fathers taking their daughters out for a birthday meal, husbands who patently bore their wives into the ground, and nervous young men who have managed to persuade a particularly attractive girl to go out to dinner and who are evidently not candidates for a second date.

Eye-catching is an old but very useful technique. Once you've settled on the woman you want, cast a quick look in her direction. Then another, longer look. A few minutes later, give her a long, even stare, until she becomes aware of your interest. It is at that moment that you will know whether you are in with an even chance or not. If she looks away and never looks in your direction again, you might have problems. If she meets your stare with a lingering glance and shows *some* interest, *no matter how faint,* you are on your way.

It's not easy to acquire the art of banter with girls. Some of us are lucky enough to have a glib loquacity that can keep a woman's attention even when we're talking absolute horseshit. Whatever you decide to say, however, say it as though you mean it, and never ever apologize for what you come out with. You can apologize to your wife, your boss, or your mistress of twenty years' standing—but when you're on the prowl, anything goes, and you've got to prove your confidences and your decisiveness in a matter of seconds.

If you're at a dance or a party, it's easy enough to ask a girl to dance. Don't take No for an answer unless you absolutely have to. A friend of mine, if rebuffed, used to claim that he had a new artificial leg, and that this was the first dance he'd been to since his amputation. This ploy immediately aroused curiosity and sympathy, and it was only when he and his newfound partner were dancing cheek-to-cheek that he would reveal himself as a liar.

"I thought you said you had an artificial leg," they'd say. "I can't feel it."

"Oh, I haven't really got one," he used to say. "I just dance as though I have."

In other milieus, however, you obviously can't ask a woman to dance. But you can still *ask* her something. Women love being asked their advice, their opinion, their views on anything. A favorite technique of another friend I knew, who did a great deal of traveling, was to approach attractive women in airport lounges and ask them if they could help him choose a duty-free perfume for his mother. Choosing perfume, with all its exposed wrists and heady smells, is quite an intimate undertaking, and it would give him all the introduction he needed.

In restaurants, you usually have a little more time for eye-catching, but the moments available for talking are extremely brief and can be dangerous. Don't be corny and send over a drink to the lady's table. This is stilted and silly, and she probably doesn't feel like another drink anyway. I have seen this happen a couple of times in restaurants, and all that happens is that the woman drinks her drink, while the donor smiles and waves from his lonely table. When the woman has finished her drink, she gets up and goes, just as she intended to all along.

Another technique that in its way is just as corny, but is far more discreet and effective, is to write your name and telephone number on a card, stroll over to the lady's table when her escort is taking a leak, and say simply: "Excuse me for interrupting, but I think you have just the face for my record album. Could you call me tomorrow?"

She might say, "Fuck off," but again she might not, and at least you've done your duty as a perfect lover. Always take the risk, always go for the slender chance, always *work* at what you're doing. If a woman's worth having, she's worth making an effort for, and keep in the front of your mind at all times the perfect lover's motto: "Women are just as attracted to men as men are to women."

What do you do if she actually does call up, eager to have her picture on Greatest Rock Hits Vol. 2? Ask her out to lunch, admit your deception at once, but flatter her solidly all the time. Again, it might turn out to be nothing more than a pleasant lunch, but it's work, work, work. The more you practice this kind of technique, the more confident you'll become, and the more confident you become, the better you'll get.

Suppose you've managed to catch a woman's attention. You have very little time, but you want to fix a date with her, or stop her from going home to her chaste bed, Ovaltine, and hot-water bottle. What the hell do you talk about?

You can be silly, bizarre, or eccentric in your conversation, but above all you must be memorable and *funny*. If you can make her laugh, you've done as signal a service to your sex life as folding back the bedsheets.

Say something like: "I've always wanted to go out with a girl like you, but my mother wouldn't let me. This is the first time in two years I've been out without her. She's so possessive, she hides my trousers to stop me going out."

It's ridiculous, this kind of line, but you'd be amazed how often it actually works. A girl wants to feel that a man is carefree, humorous, and fun. She wants to know that he is attracted to her, but she doesn't want closely knit eyebrows and heavy breathing. There are one or two men who can get away with the serious bit—men who are built like Victor Mature and have smoky, basso voices, but even they have to resort to humor and teasing from time to time.

Exercise Four:

Take a pen and a pad, and sketch yourself out a few topics of conversation. Start reading newspapers more closely, build up a memory bank of interesting tidbits of information and opinions. On any one day, at any one time, make sure you have at least three amusing things you can talk about, even if you've had to learn them almost parrot-fashion. Keep your eyes and your ears open for quotable quotations and humorous one-line sayings. Try and come up with some lesser-known all-purpose ambiguous statements to fill in those conversation gaps. One remark that I have always found gets a laugh, even though I'm quite convinced that most people haven't got a clue what it means, is: "As one judge said to the other: 'Be just, and if you can't be just, be arbitrary.' " Another all-purpose saying is: "It is better to be without bread than without a remedy." It's all persiflage, all nonsense, but it sounds impressive at those crucial moments in pick-up conversation when you're going to need impressiveness most.

Now, all this is leading up to one thing.

Sexual intercourse.

This is where you have to sit back for a while and work out your emotional attitudes, using the questionnaire I set out in Chapter One. Before you go off on the prowl, you have to be quite sure in your own mind that bed is what you want. You also have to be quite sure that, within reason, you're going to get it.

If you don't find a girl that you like, for God's sake don't spend the whole evening traipsing around, lowering your sights with each successive disappointment until you find you're following anything down a badly lit sidestreet. An evening like that can destroy your confidence for a month. It's not good for you, and it's beneath you, so stop it.

When an evening turns out to be a dud, womanwise, go home and pour yourself a stiff drink, read an interesting book, and go to bed. If you feel physically frustrated, take a pornographic magazine into bed with you and masturbate. There's much more dignity in that than in shuffling dejectedly after talent you don't really want.

But make sure before any evening that you're convinced of your desire and your right to try and get a woman into bed with you. If you feel guilty or hung up about it, work out why. Don't go looking around for a fuck to give you solace from some other problem. Go out and get in there because it's enjoyable, because *she's* going to enjoy it, and because it may be the start of a wonderful, wonderful friendship.

Who knows, you may even be unlucky enough to get married.

Now we come to that tricky little point that I'm asked about more than almost anything else.

How do you get a woman into bed with you?

The answer is *planning* and *continuity*. It's got nothing to do with a magic phrase, or a magic technique. It's got everything to do with good stage-management.

The first evening that you take a girl out, use your head. Don't ask her where she wants to go, or what she wants to do. You're paying for it, and she's relying on your taste and discretion. Use that taste and discretion to your sexual advantage.

Take her to a very good restaurant—preferably one with a bar. Have a few drinks before eating, and give yourself the chance to loosen up and relax. Don't forget to tell her how lovely she looks. Girls may blush and get all uncomfortable when you flatter them, but that's only because they're not used to it—so many men have lost the art.

Eat, for Christ's sake, a *light* meal. More seductions have foundered on bearnaise sauce and two helpings of dessert than I care to think about. Try a good fish, like trout, with a crisp white wine, like Pouilly Fuissé or Montrachet. Avoid garlic, onions, spices.

If it's summer, select a quiet and romantic spot and go for a walk afterward. Even in cities, there's usually a river or a park to stroll in. If it's winter, go to a discotheque or a bar where there's plenty of life. Do not under any circumstances go to the movies. You're supposed to be getting to know each other, getting attracted to each other. There's no point in sitting in the dark, both facing the same way looking at moving pictures of people who are bound to be more attractive than you are.

At the close of the evening, try and ensure that you are much nearer to where *you* live than to where *she* lives. Maybe you've been clever enough to talk about a fantastic book you've been reading—in which case, why doesn't she come up and borrow it, and have some coffee at the same time? I think actually that coffee must be the greatest aphrodisiac beverage of all time, since every girl who gets laid must have at least one cup in her at the time.

So, you go to your place. Is it ready? It is clean and neat? Is it *too* clean and neat? You don't want the place to look as though you've got it ready for her specially, do you? *Don't* put out coffee cups all prepared. *Don't* turn down the corner of the bed or have a clean towel all ready for her in the bathroom, just make the place look as though a clean, reasonably neat human being lives there, and has just unexpectedly invited a woman back for coffee.

Now don't be slow about kissing her. There's nothing worse than those minutes and sometimes hours of agony as the man creeps nearer and nearer along the couch, trying to make up his mind that now is the time to lunge forward with a desperate kiss.

Put the coffee on, turn around, put your arms around her, and kiss her. If she's come as far as this, she undoubtedly won't fight you off. If she does, keep cool, make the coffee, put some music on, and when you sit down with her, *cuddle up*. The farther you put yourself away from her to begin with, the farther you've got to go later.

Kiss her, caress her, turn her on (more about all this

heated stuff later). If you're really a perfect lover, you won't have to get her into bed. She'll want it right there and then on the living-room floor.

Later in the book I'll tell you how to get love-juice stains out of rugs.

FOUR:

Lick Like a Butterfly, Bite Like a Bee

The trouble with foreplay is that most people think it should only happen *before,* not *during* or *after.*

Foreplay, however, should be happening all the time. It would be more accurate, in fact, to call it "love-play." The purpose of it is not just to get your bedmate into a sufficient state of excitement to insert your well-trained penis (see Chapter Two), but to keep her in an ever-mounting condition of erotic excitement all through your sexual activities.

As part of your training as a perfect lover, start thinking about your fingers, your mouth, your feet, and your body as sexual organs, as well as your penis. They are all capable of giving and receiving erotic stimulation, even when your erection is temporarily out of service. Make love with the whole of yourself, not just those few cubic inches of flesh between your legs.

What makes sex erotic, as I've said before, and will probably say again, is *surprise.* Doing unusual things at times they're not expected. I was talking in Hyannis, Massachusetts, to a man who was complaining that he no longer got any pleasure out of sex with his wife. I asked him

46

what was the last sexy thing she had done to him—the last that he could remember anyway.

"The time that really sticks in my mind," he said, "was when we were screwing one night. We were in the middle of screwing, when she suddenly put her hand around and started fondling my balls. She kept on stroking and squeezing them until I got my rocks off. She never did it again, and I never felt I could ask her. I mean, what do you say: 'Please squeeze my balls?' She would have thought I was a pervert."

That was a very simple and elementary caress for a wife to give to her husband, and it's not saying much for their sexual relationship that she never did it before or since. But the point is that within the context of their lovemaking, this bit of play came as a pleasurable surprise, and the man could picture it in his mind for a long time afterward. Just think of the effect you could have on a girl if you could do something like that *every* time.

Sexual intercourse is a strangely forgettable experience. Once those brief seconds of intense pleasure are over, and you've got your clothes on again, it's often hard to believe that it's actually happened. It needs the unexpected to make it stick in the mind, and foreplay is the sexual art of the unexpected.

Every girl knows when she climbs into bed with sex on her mind that pole will go into hole. What she doesn't know is what *else* is going to happen.

Here's an airline stewardess talking—a reasonably experienced girl of twenty-three whom I met while interviewing girls about their sexual habits:

"I didn't realize until I slept with Michael what a sensitive back I had. You somehow don't think of your back as being sexy. But when we first went to bed together, after we'd kissed and fondled each other a little, he quite gently turned me over so I was lying on my stomach.

"He nuzzled the back of my neck, then started kissing and licking me on my shoulders and down my spine. I'd never felt anything like it before. I just didn't know how many sexy nerves there were in your back. I could feel his breath on me, too, and that made it even more tickly and exciting.

"He slowly worked his way down my backbone, kissing and licking and pinching me with his teeth, until he got to the top of my butt. My skin felt so sensitive by then that I hardly knew what to do. Then he ran his tongue all the way down the crack and pushed it into my asshole. Nobody had ever done that to me before, and I remember that I shouted out loud."

She *remembered*. And you, too, can do things that girls like this will remember.

Let's turn our attention first of all to *kissing*. I hope it goes without saying that before you kiss a girl you want to get into bed, your breath is fresh and lovely, your teeth are in reasonable order, and you haven't recently been chewing rum-soaked tobacco.

Try to make your first kisses moderately dry. There is a time when you will both be kissing in the heat of passion, and the saliva will run out of your mouths. But to begin with, few girls want to feel that they've made a date with a bulldog. Explore her teeth with your tongue, running the tip delicately around twixt her lips and gums, and enjoy a little playful combat with her own tongue.

Don't loiter around the mouth too long. What you're doing with those first kisses is trying to make a sensitive sexy feeling spread all over her, and you won't do that by hogging her lips. Kiss her cheeks, ears, neck. Make sure you hold her warmly and closely during all this. She wants to feel your powerful masculine body against hers, with all its security and strength, and its pungent smell of Harris tweed and pipes. If you don't wear tweed or smoke a pipe, don't worry about it. The security and strength is enough.

Love bites? If you've both unbottled something really hot and heavy in the first few minutes then you can try one or two Dracula forays to the lower neck. But generally, I recommend you stay away from these until you're well into the bedroom. Unless a girl is moderately turned on, she might object to both the pain of love bites and also the telltale evidence they provide.

Perfect lovers never ever bite a married woman, unless she is married to *them*.

When the kisses are simmering nicely, get those hands working. Start off by holding her sweet little head in your powerful manly palms, then run your hands down her back, around her waist, and up toward her breasts. Don't be afraid to caress her breasts. She might be a little shy at first, and try to push you away, but if you do it firmly and sensitively, she shouldn't object.

You may well have a hard-on by this time. If you've got it, use it. Don't press it up against her as though you're sticking up a bank cashier. Brush it against her thighs once or twice, just enough to let her know you're in heat. The very thought that she's turned you on goes a long way toward turning a girl on herself.

Caress her thighs, and if she's wearing a skirt or dress, slide your hand up the *outside* of her thigh and stroke her hip and side. Then get your fingers inside her panties and knead her bottom with ever increasing vibrancy. If you can reach, touch the cleft of her bottom and even the lips of her vagina with your fingertips.

Depending on how willing she is, this is where you start undressing her. And this is also where a lot of imperfect lovers make their gaucheness very obvious. If you can't undress a girl quickly and effectively, you're liable to screw up your whole seduction, and change your image from suave man-of-the-world to butterfingered buffoon quicker than you can say "Hooks and eyes."

Women's clothes are very odd, and undo in lots of unusual and difficult ways. They're hard enough for women to get in and out of—notice the number of times that they wander into the room, begging plaintively for someone to "Zip me up, please." For men, who are used to big buttons and simple catches, clothes with tight sleeves and a side zipper, four hooks, and sixteen small buttons can be a nightmare.

Exercise Five:
Make a study, and take notes, on the ways in which various dresses, slacks, brassieres, dungarees, panty hose (if you're unlucky), and other women's garments do up and undo. Look at every girl in the street and see what kind of clothes she's wearing, making a mental note on how to take them off. If you have a secretary or know some other girl you can talk to on a purely friendly basis, make inquiries about any new and baffling garment she might be wearing: "How the hell do you get into *that*?"

The perfect lover always treats a girl's clothes with respect. Whatever you've read in stag magazines about ripping away blouses, skirts, and filmy nylon, forget it. Clothes are expensive and girls take a lot of trouble to find them. Tights are expensive as well, so make sure your nails are cut. These may all sound like nitpicking details, but they can make all the difference between a smooth undressing-sequence and an embarrassing shambles.

There are many different schools of thought on whether a man should undress himself or let the girl undress him, but if you're talking about a first date, then for me there is only one answer. *Take your own clothes off.* Shirt first, *then* shoes and socks, *then* trousers and underpants. You can be much quicker than she can, and you are placing no responsibility on her for what is happening. If she has no responsibility, it's much more difficult for her to get cold feet.

Don't forget that order of stripping-off, either. There are few more hilarious spectacles than a man who is stark naked except for his socks. You want the girl to be happy and laughing—but *with* you, not *at* you.

After the undressing bit, the love-play can continue in earnest. And you now have the whole of her nude body, and yours, as a playground.

During this next stage of lovemaking, your restraint and self-control can alter your bedmate's whole attitude toward you, both physically and psychologically. Much as you want to get your penis into her, it is one of the greatest talents of the perfect lover to hold back from entry as long as he humanly can. To put it rather coldly, this is so that the girl, when he finally enters her, will be in such a state of anticipation and arousal that she will feel a deep sense of *relief* (for the sake of Women's Lib, I won't say gratitude).

The best way I ever heard this technique described was in the autobiography of Charlie Mingus, the black progressive jazz musician. He quoted an older man's sexual advice to him when he was just thirteen years old:

"What this old man told me was, for those who don't have the natural talent, here's some good rules for fucking. Kiss her. Play with her awhile, then insert your peppermint stick, just the knob, the head of it. Rub it all up her split for a long time over the clitoris, in just a little bit and out, from bottom to top and around until she's warming up to you. You gonna make love like this for hours, kissing, playing, sucking her breasts and fingering that good pussy till she's begging for you. Then you don't just ram it in. You put the head in sorta gentle and easy. After it's good and moist, seeping all through the sheets, you don't give her all that white-folk freaky stuff. Just plain old good fucking. The best position that old man found was on one side with her on her back, 'cause he was a big man. She's just about dying from waiting now, but you're just teasing, gradually giving it to her. Stay in for just a little while to let her know what kind of sweets you got but pull back if she reaches up for it, all the way out and around the edges of the lips. Then all of a sudden you hit it hard and deep as you can and hold it there firm and tight and rock from side to side. Then draw back, almost out. Tease. Move every which way but so easy she can barely feel it move. Tighten and loosen its muscles. That gives her a throbbing sensation. She'll start reaching for it again. Pull away. Just when she gives up and settles on her ass, hit it in hard and deep as you can, draw it out fast and hit it quick again. Don't move for an instant after it's all the way in.

"Hold it tight and rock, then draw it out again easy. This time let her soft flesh cling to you—she'll try to follow and keep it up inside her. Now she starts to beg you and everything to hit it for her like you just did. Don't do it. Just play and tease some more. If she ain't never done anything like this, she'll start getting frantic, crying and begging. Then—when you make up your mind to—let her have it again, hard, fast, and deep. Hit it and hold it in there and rock from side to side, kiss her and hold her in your steady rock. Then ease it back and pretend you're gonna quit. Take it out. And if she don't grab you and plead and beg you to please fuck her *your* way then you can have one of them Cadillacs sitting out there! . . ."

The penis exercises you've been doing since Chapter Two should help you keep control of your feelings as you "rein-in" like this. And if you concentrate on working *her* up, while putting your own sexual desires into the background, your technique, once perfected, should be devastating.

Here are a few things to be doing while she comes steadily to the boil. Please note that all these exercises *do* require a female assistant.

Exercise Six:
While caressing her breasts with your hands, take one nipple between your lips. Suck it gently into your mouth and roll it around your palate with your tongue. Nip it *carefully* with your teeth. When the nipple is stiff, push it with the end of your tongue into the soft tissue of the breast, and try to close the surrounding areola over it with your lips.

Exercise Seven:
Kiss and nip her stomach and hips with your teeth. When I say nip, I don't mean draw blood—just a light bite with your front fangs. Run your tongue across her stomach just above her pubic hair, then down the crease of the top of her thigh until you are licking her in the hollow between the inside of her leg and the outer lip of her vagina. *Don't* touch the actual clitoris or vagina with your tongue—just flick it across the perineum, which is the

bridge between the vagina and the anus, to the other side. Then lick her in the other hollow between leg and vaginal lip.

Exercise Eight:

Caress the whole of her vaginal area with the three first fingers of your left hand. As her vagina becomes moist, or if it is moist already, slide your middle finger *slowly* into her vagina. See how far it will reach. You should be able to touch her cervix, the neck of her womb, which will give her an intense nervous sensation. Next, slide in your index finger alongside your middle finger. Manipulate her gently, but remember that the vaginal tissues are delicate, and that clean, short fingernails are *essential*. When your fingers are really slippery, take them out, and quickly but carefully push your index finger into her anus and your thumb into her vagina. You now have a grip on the thin and sensitive wall of skin between her bottom and her vagina, and a few discreet tugs on this can produce electrifying results.

While you are trying out these basic exercises, remind yourself constantly that you have other fingers and other limbs which should all be doing their bit to arouse your bedmate. While your left hand probes her vagina, for example, your right hand should be caressing her face and hair and neck in a more romantic way. Your feet can be brushing against the inside of her calves, your erect penis against her side. Use your *hair* as well. Men are always raving on about women's hair without thinking about the erotic effects that their own can give. Brush her breast with it, rub it against her thighs. Your hair is the best French tickler there's ever been, and its natural.

Even if you're hairless, your scalp can be useful. In J. P. Donleavy's novel *The Beastly Beatitudes of Baltha-*

zar B, the hero's uncle recommends highly the delights of *frottage* with a bald head against a woman's breasts.

What about more unusual love play? This account comes from a long tape-recording I made with a nineteen-year-old American girl about her affairs with older men.

"After we'd been cuddling each other some, he kind of moved down the bed and started kissing me down the back of my legs. I'm usually very ticklish, but it was pretty sexy as well. I was lying on my side, and he was lying on his side kind of facing me, only the other way up, so his face was right by my feet. And do you know what he did ... he started *sucking my toes.* You know, that sounds really weird, but if you've ever had anyone do it to you ... well, it sent like *shivers* all the way up my back.

"He slipped a toe into his mouth and licked it and sucked it, and kept squiggling his tongue in between them. Then he kind of held me really close to him so that his prick was sticking between my legs right against my pussy, and I could put my hand down and rub and press his prick up against me. And all the time he went on licking my toes. Can you imagine your *feet* feeling sexy? Well, mine did. ..."

The toe technique (officially called "shrimping") is something you might reserve for a third or fourth date. And since we've been talking about hair, here's one that could also work on a later night. It was told to me by an author who is so well known that it would be embarrassing to mention his name.

"It was on one of those very rare occasions when you meet a girl and both of you are equally infatuated," he explained. "We took a taxi back to my apartment, and we were naked and into bed in double-quick time. She was a rather unusual-looking girl, with very long reddish hair. Titian, I think you might call it, if you were being fussy. Her name was Sandra.

"As we started thrashing about on the bed, I had an extraordinary urge to thrust my cock *in her hair*. Without thinking about it, I moved up the bed, turned her on her side and did just that. I wrapped her hair all around my cock and balls, and sort of massaged her scalp with them. I think it turned her on even more than it did me. She went quite wild, and started almost shampooing herself with me, and then rubbing my cock against her face and cheeks, still tangled round with hair."

When you are actually having intercourse, your hands should keep busy. Caress her face, breasts, and body. Hold her bottom and stimulate the parted lips of her vagina. Gently massage her clitoris, and slip the tip of your finger into her anus. Think all the time of giving *her* pleasure, and your own will come even more intensely and more naturally. The perfect lover, like the perfect gentleman, is above all *considerate,* and he is constantly devising ways to maximize his partner's enjoyment.

After intercourse, the perfect lover remains alert to his bedmate's wants with continuing love-play. If she hasn't managed to reach a climax, he will massage her clitoris for her to give her satisfaction. Not all girls feel the need to have an orgasm every time they make love, and it's possible she will feel she's had enough without being aroused any further. But nonetheless the perfect lover will make the effort—only stopping when she takes his hand away or closes her thighs against his caresses.

Cuddle your bedmate after making love, and don't be afraid to compliment her on the way she screws. Kiss her a lot, and flatter her as much as you feel like. It's worth remembering that women are just as worried about their performance in bed as men—even though the onus for good lovemaking is traditionally on the male. I don't know how many times I've heard girls say apologetically, as they climb into bed: "I'm not very experienced, you know." So don't forget to reassure her that she has satisfied you—and even though you don't have to say it in so many words, give her the impression that she could very well be the best lay you've ever had.

Once you're outside the bedroom again, don't ignore your love-play. Women like to feel physically attractive all the time, not just during intercourse. It amazes me to see how many men never touch or caress their wives or girl friends during daylight hours. The perfect lover, which you are going to be, is constantly and demonstrably affectionate. He will put his arm around his girl friend when they're in the company of others, and give her a squeeze. He'll hold her hand when they're out walking. He'll kiss her while they wait for the traffic lights to change. It may all sound impossibly corny, but women appreciate and enjoy impossibly corny gestures. They still like bunches of flowers and surprise presents. They still like having doors opened for them. And they still like a man to show, *especially publicly,* that he's fond of them. Successful sex has got a great deal more to do with this kind of backup operation than it has to do with plain fucking. Anyone can fuck. Not everyone can be a perfect lover.

FIVE:

If Food Be the Food of Love . . .

When astronauts are in training for space flights, they go for high-protein foods like steak and eggs. When Eastern gurus are in training for meditation, they eat simple unworldly foods like brown rice and lentils.

You're in training for perfect lovership, and since the fitness of your body for the emotional and physical stresses of sex is of prime importance, you will find it a help to diet accordingly.

It's back to the mirror again, I'm afraid. Undress and take stock of your shape. Is it attractive to look at, from a girl's point of view? Is your skin clear and your waist trim? Or are there signs of a soft potbelly and a spare tire?

You don't have to look like Charles Atlas (R.I.P.). In fact, many girls are positively turned off by overdeveloped muscles. It's not actually very often that you have sand kicked in your face on the beach, and if it does happen, you can always wait until the bully's back is turned and hit him over the head with a pail full of wet sand.

But you should be moderately streamlined. Apart from preserving your looks, remember that sexual intercourse is a short, sharp, strenuous activity, and any extra weight is most unwelcome for bursts of energy-burning like that.

The perfect lover should at least be able to run 200 yards at full speed without gasping for breath. Once you can do that, you will know that your body is toned up for the maximum enjoyment of sex.

Before I set out a suggested diet for the improvement of your erotic performance, I'd like to take a look at aphrodisiacs.

The subject of aphrodisiacs comes up time and time again during discussions on sex. Many men still believe that there are drugs and foods which can magically restore their erections, or which can turn a docile librarian into a raging nymphomaniac at the drop of a pill.

There is *nothing* which, taken alone, can achieve these highly desirable ends. If you don't believe me, this is what the *Encyclopaedia Britannica* has to say about it: "In spite of their vast popularity, almost no scientific studies have been written about [aphrodisiacs]. Of the various foods to which aphrodisiac powers are traditionally attributed, fish, vegetables, and spices have been the most popular throughout history. None of these foods, however, contains any chemical agents that could affect a direct physiological reaction upon the genitourinary tract, and it must be concluded that the reputation of various supposedly erotic foods is based not upon fact but upon folklore."

Some very notable names have tried all kinds of different foods and potions throughout history in a search for improved potency. Louis XIV girded his loins for bed with a cup of orange water with a teaspoonful of sugar and a dash of distilled spirit. Madame du Barry sprinkled her chocolates with ambergris powder, and many Elizabethans ate a candy made of the root of sea holly.

The classic magic cure for impotence was an extraordinary potion made of the following ingredients: 2 ounces of concentrated Roumi opium, 2 ounces of cinnamon, 3 cloves, 3 cardamom seeds, 1 sprig of fresh ginger, 1 dehydrated mountain lizard, 1 shake of white pepper, all stewed in olive oil with mace, coriander, and frankincense.

It may work; I can't tell you for sure, though, because I had trouble dehydrating my lizard.

You may prefer Louis XV's sex salad, made from crawfish tails, truffles, the heart of a lettuce, and shrimp puree. Plovers' eggs and roosters' kidneys, crushed with artichoke, bacon, and truffles, are also said to be aphrodisiacs.

But the *Encyclopaedia Britannica* is pretty pessimistic on the subject: "Since food cannot produce sexual desire biochemically, the question at once arises of how it has happened that man has, for centuries, in all parts of the world, attributed such power to foods. It should be remembered that a large number of the plants, vegetables, spices, etc., that are supposed to be aphrodisiac acquired their reputation many centuries ago, when there was no scientific information available."

So there. But the *Encyclopaedia* does go on to say that modern science does recognize that cantharis and yohimbine are both technically aphrodisiacs.

The sad thing about yohimbine, which is made from the bark of the African yohimbe tree, is that it only has an erotically stimulatory effect when taken in fatal doses. There isn't much fun to be had from terminal intercourse.

Cantharis (Spanish Fly) is just as bad. It is a poison which causes irritation and blistering of the alimentary and renal tracts. Casanova once slipped a dose of it to a couple of women in a brothel he was visiting. One died on the spot and the other was in such agony that she hurled herself to her death from an upper window. Hardly a suave, sophisticated evening out.

Aphrodisiac claims have been made for marijuana and hashish, but since both are quite powerful sedatives, it's rather difficult to see what they could do for an already sedate young lady. The same goes for LSD.

You may have noticed many advertisements for various pills for the "improvement of sexual energy." These usually contain such startling ingredients as caffeine, milk powder, hops, lecithin, hawthorn hips, the Korean root ginseng, and all kinds of other harmless but hardly stimulating chemicals and herbs. You can take them if they make you feel any better, but malted milk tablets are just as effective in most cases, and a great deal cheaper.

In spite of the fact that there aren't any foods or drugs which can turn either you or her on instantly, there are plenty of diets which can improve your general physical condition and, in association with the exercises and suggestions in the rest of this book, can actively contribute to your sexual stamina.

Although your stressful civilized life probably makes it difficult, try to eat light meals at regular intervals.

Have *something* for breakfast—a glass of fresh orange juice, a raw egg stirred up with Worcestershire Sauce and pepper, and a cup of black coffee. If you can't stomach raw eggs, try a bowl of a granola-type cereal with a little milk.

Keep off alcohol as much as you can without ruining your social life. Alcoholic drinks make you feel very happy, but they ruin your waistline, your appetite, and your nervous responses. Wine is less fattening than beer and spirits.

At lunchtime, avoid sandwiches and pies and other quick foods. Have a salad if you have time; if not, eat some cheese, crackers, and apples. At four o'clock, have a cup of black coffee or tea with lemon and a spoonful of honey.

In the evening, unless you're going out for a special dinner, avoid rich fatty foods and potatoes. If you want an alcoholic nightcap, stir yourself up a potent dose of Scotch with hot water, two spoonfuls of honey, and a squeeze of lemon.

You don't have to become a health addict, but there are certain foods that are just as easy to get hold of as ordinary products, and which contain far greater nutriment in each bite. Try and stay away from white breads and mass-produced breakfast cereals, both of which contain about as much nourishment as the paper they're wrapped in (in fact, if your stomach was capable of digesting it, you'd get more goodness out of cardboard cornflake boxes than you would out of the cornflakes).

If you eat more fresh fruit, vegetables, whole-grained bread, and other food with fiber and roughage, your digestive system will function better, you will feel less sluggish and unfit, and when you get into bed with sex on your mind, your body will respond more readily to the demands you put on it.

You will probably live longer as well.

Exercise Nine:
For 12 weeks, starting from today, eat lightly and regularly. Avoid potatoes and starchy foods whenever possible. Cut down your alcohol intake to no more than three glasses of whiskey or wine or two pints of beer a day. Stop eating candies and cakes, and start using artificial sweeteners in tea and coffee. If you feel a desperate need

for sweet foods, take glucose or honey, cut down on fried foods, and look for grilled or broiled meats on restaurant menus.

Compared to what you are eating now, this might seem like a very hard regime. But there will come a time—sooner than you think—when your lean and fitter-feeling body will look more exciting, and start working more excitingly, in bed.

SIX:

Out of the Mouths . . .

In his otherwise very jolly book on sex techniques, *The Book of Love,* Dr. David Delvin, who has something in excess of twenty-nine letters after his name, says that cunnilingus, which "simply means kissing your partner's vulva," is "relatively easy to master in a fairly short time."

He goes on: "Simply bend downwards and apply a few kisses to the upper part of your mate's pubic hair. Gently move your lips an inch or two downwards until you are in the area of the clitoris (your partner's enthusiastic reaction should tell you that you're in the right spot). Then use your lips and tongue to bring her to a high pitch of excitement. Your tongue should slide back and forth over the clitoris in a regular movement, very much as you would do with your finger."

This isn't a bad basic description of cunnilingus, but Dr. David has omitted one or two fundamental details of technique which the perfect lover should have at the tip of his tongue.

Cunnilingus doesn't mean "simply kissing your partner's vulva." As its dog-latin name suggests, it means "cunt-tongue"—all the different ways of arousing a woman's genitals with your mouth, lips, tongue, and teeth. If you're a lover with any pretensions to perfection, you will have dozens of different ways of stimulating your bedmate's vulva.

The perfect lover looks at cunnilingus in two ways. He sees it as a *complement* to intercourse—as part of the love-play that arouses his partner to readiness for coitus. Or he sees it as an *alternative* to intercourse, a way in which he can bring her to orgasm at times when he can't, or doesn't want to, make love.

The techniques used in each of these two ways are substantially different. Bringing a woman to a climax by cunnilingus requires steady, rhythmic, uninterrupted clitoral licking. When you're simply turning her on, you can use a whole variety of licks, sucks, nips, and rubs.

Your tongue, like the rest of you, needs to be in good shape for cunnilingus. When you're trying to get a woman off by lick alone, you may have to work at it, quickly and consistently, for up to a quarter of an hour.

Exercise Ten:
Take an orange, slice it in half, and lick at it with the tip of your tongue for fifteen minutes. Suck up any juice that drops as it falls. Do this exercise once every other day for three weeks, until you can lick at the orange almost endlessly without tongue fatigue.

Another technique that the perfect lover must acquire is that of breathing properly during oral sex. If you're a good swimmer, you'll be halfway toward acquiring the necessary skill. When your face is buried deep between a girl's legs, respiration can be a problem, especially if she's the type who tends to keep her thighs together. The trick is to breathe in through the nose, through the pubic hair if she's got any, and exhale through the mouth—not directly into the vagina but down the cleft of her bottom.

Incidentally, even though it's an often-repeated warning, it's worth saying again that you should never blow air into a girl's vagina. There's a possibility that it could cause an air bubble in the blood through the absorbent lining of the womb, and if the bubble traveled to the brain through the circulatory system, it could kill her. Perfect lovers never kill their bedmate.

Don't let your girl friend blow down your penis, either. It could damage your urinary tubes, and no experience is worth that. Dr. Eugene Schoenfeld, the San Francisco-based sex adviser who writes under the name of "Dr. Hippocrates," once received a letter from a man who was rather concerned because his girl friend had snipped a hole through his scrotum with nail scissors, and turned him on by inflating his balls through a straw. Needless to say, to breathe mouth bacteria inside one of the most sensitive parts of the body is sheer madness.

The perfect lover brings his woman to a climax through cunnilingus by seeking out the most sensitive spot around her clitoris with the tip of his tongue. Different women have different sensations in their clitoris, and what arouses one may frustrate another. There is nothing more irritating than being *nearly* turned on, as you'll know from experience if a woman has ever tried to rub your penis to orgasm and has never quite managed to get the right grip.

Some women like having the upper part of the clitoris licked in a downward direction. Others prefer having the underside of it licked upward. You may be able to tell which your bedmate enjoys more by the way she squirms and sighs under the ministrations of your probing tongue—but if you're not sure, don't be worried about asking. She'll appreciate your efforts to hit her right on the spot marked "X," and a few seconds' muffled conversation won't turn either of you off.

If you want to get her to orgasm with cunnilingus, the principal word of advice I can give you is to *persist*. Eventually she will be overwhelmed by the sensations you're giving her, and even if you suffer from rampant aching of the jaws afterward, you'll be her friend for life. Or at least for as long as you want her.

When you're using oral sex simply as part of your *love-play*, to get her juiced up enough for eventual penetration, you can be a great deal more inventive. Lead into your vulva attack with Exercise Seven—licking the outer lips of her cunt first, then gradually maneuvering your way to the inner lips. When it looks as though she's really beginning to enjoy herself, thrust your stiffened tongue deep into her vagina a few times. Then relax your tongue again, and slide it ever so carefully and delicately upward—exerting a little pressure on her urethral opening, and finally reaching the clitoris.

Strum the clitoris with your tongue a few times—licking quickly backward and forward. Then, pressing your lips closer against her, suck the clitoris and its moist surrounding flesh right into your mouth. Ease the stiffening clitoris against your palate, rubbing it from side to side—and all the time, keep up the suction, so that as much of her vaginal lips are in your mouth as you can hold.

When you can maintain the suction no longer, turn your attention to the inner lips and vaginal opening again, flickering your tongue around with as much enthusiasm as you like. You can even nip the lips and clitoris with your teeth, but for God's sake remember you've got highly delicate skin there.

Penetrate her vagina with your tongue again, then slowly move your way down to the perineum, and give her "a trip around the world," which means a thorough licking around the anus. Always save that as your finale, because even though a few rectal bacteria won't kill you, they can easily be transferred to the sensitive vagina and infect your girl friend with an irritating dose of monilia or some similar internal complaint. It's no fun for her, and it won't be any fun for you either, because she'll be off sex for a while.

There are all sorts of titillating extras you can add to cunnilingus. A very lovely girl I knew used to enjoy inserting a peeled banana into herself, expecting her lover to eat it out of her. All I can say is that I hope her lover had stuck to a light evening meal, because trying to be passionate with a mouthful of fruit is a little complicated.

A reader wrote to me once and claimed he had seen a private sex show in Denmark where three girls had raised their legs in the air and had radishes, grapes, and shredded cabbage pushed into their vaginas, topped off with whipped cream. Three men had then sat down and eaten the contents out of the girls with teaspoons. You can try it if you like, but it might be better to leave out the radishes.

A more practical variation was told to me by a Swedish girl who eventually had herself photographed for a magazing doing it (or having it done to her). "I was in bed one evening with my boyfriend, and we were petting with each other. He always keeps a glass of water by the bed, because after making love we are invariably very thirsty. He put his head down and started licking me out. I was really enjoying it and getting very aroused. Then all of a sudden, he lifted his head, reached over, and took a long drink of water. I laughed, because I couldn't think what he was doing.

"I soon discovered. He opened my legs up wide, and spread open my cunt with his fingers, and spurted a long jet of cold water from his mouth all over my clitoris. It really made me shiver. The whole idea turned me on more than anything and after that we had very good lovemaking."

A worried lover once asked me what he should do after cunnilingus about his juice-smeared face. "I try to wipe my face on the pillow before I kiss the girl again," he said. "I'm just not sure how they're going to take it."

Well, I'm not sure either. Some girls get very excited by kissing a man whose lips and cheeks are wet with their own lubrication—others are a little reserved about it. Personally, I'm in favor of it—I think it's very sexy, and is part of the complete abandon that perfect lovers, both men and women, should experience during lovemaking. Even though many men may wrinkle up their noses, I'm equally in favor of the man kissing the girl after she's brought him to a climax through fellatio. Sexual fluids are pretty nondescript, tastewise and odorwise, when they're fresh, and there are more germs on a ham sandwich you buy at your local lunch counter.

This brings us to the knotty subject of cock-sucking. Since most books of sexual technique describe lovemaking from both the male and female points of view, they tend to omit any discussion of a man's most difficult problem when it comes to fellatio—or rather, when it comes to *wanting* fellatio.

Cardinal rule one: *never* ask a girl to suck your penis. This will completely ruin the spontaneity of what, for most girls, is an extremely intimate caress. Just think of the sign you see in some grocery stores: "Please do not ask for credit, as refusal may offend."

The same applies to cardinal rule two. Never force a girl's head down toward your penis in the hope that she'll get the message and start fellating. A lot of girls have told me that this was their introduction to oral sex, and that it took them a long time to get over the feeling of being forced, and yet at the same time feeling obligated. Perfect lovers never make their bedmates feel obligated to do anything—they make them feel they want to do it because they want to return his erotic favors with interest.

So, if you find yourself in bed with a girl who is either so inexperienced that she has never taken a man's penis in her mouth before, or who just doesn't seem inclined to do it, this is what to do.

Start kissing her breasts and her stomach and finally her vulva, and as you do so, twist yourself around so that you are lying the opposite way from her—with your feet at the head of the bed. Your cock will now be in reasonable proximity to her mouth. Don't dangle it in front of her like a carrot in front of an obstinate mule—don't even let the possibility that she might take it between her lips enter your mind. Just enjoy your cunnilinguine down at your end, and *leave the decision entirely up to her.* She's got the opportunity, she's got the motivation, and so you have as good a chance as you'll ever have. If she doesn't take the bait this time, she'll take it eventually. Don't show that you're disappointed or disgruntled if she doesn't do it this time. The day will dawn, *mes amis,* the day will dawn.

When she does start licking and sucking your penis, she may need a little help. Some girls are wary of fellatio because they're never sure whether they're doing it right or not.

Don't shove it down her throat. She's not a cask of Benedictine that needs instant stoppering. Whatever you've read about Linda Lovelace and her "sword-swallowing" activities in *Deep Throat,* that kind of up-to-the-balls ingestion takes a great deal of practice in breathing and suppressing a human being's normal gag reflex.

Let her tongue and suck the fireman's helmet, holding yourself so that she doesn't plunge too much in her mouth at first. Don't be afraid to whisper to her that cock-sucking doesn't have to mean actually *sucking*—not like a stick of rock candy anyway. With gentle to-and-fro movements, demonstrate how her lips and tongue can titillate their way up and down the shaft of your cock.

While all this is happening, don't let those hands and fingers rest. Remember your love-play. Caress her lips as she's actually holding your penis in her mouth, and run your other hand through her hair.

If she's bringing you to a climax, don't spring a load of sperm on her by surprise. You might feel desperately that you want her to drink your ejaculation, but don't force it on her. It's more trouble than it's worth.

An erstwhile friend of mine held a girl's ears to stop her moving away as he shot his wad, and instantly regretted it. She was extremely ill all over his satin sheets.

All you have to say is: "I'm coming"—well in time for her to make up her mind whether she wants to swallow or not.

If she does swallow—or even if she doesn't—give her a cuddle and a kiss afterward. She might have sperm on her lips, but if she's not too disgusted to have it in her mouth, why should you be? It's not like eating a slice off your own buttocks.

For the chemically minded, my friend Robert Chartham, author of more books on sexual manners than anyone I can think of, describes the content of semen as follows: "Fructose [simple sugar], very high concentrations of citric acid, vitamin C, and other chemical substances, including many enzymes."

It doesn't even contain monosodium glutamate, so it can't be that bad.

When I edited *Forum* magazine, there was a persistent correspondence, mainly from women readers, on the vexing topic of whether swallowing semen increased a woman's bust size. It doesn't, actually, but even when I have strenuously denied it, I have found that girls are still fascinated by the idea. So in the field of semen-swallowing, like everything else, a little psychology may work wonders for you.

Mind you, I've said nothing.

SEVEN:

Intercourse, Perfect Intercourse

So when, you might ask, do I get what I came for? After all the love-play and the cunnilingus and the fellatio, when do I get to *penetrate*?

The answer is: When she's more than ready. As I said in Chapter Four, she'll appreciate your penis sliding inside her much more if she's already gasping for it. And you yourself will have reserved your energy for a far better performance.

If you put your penis in before either of you are really aroused, you will have to pump up and down that much longer before she's at a high pitch of stimulation, and by the time you're turning the corner into the home plate, much of your strength and stamina will be drained. There's nothing like those last few seconds of fluid, frenzied fucking—but they're so much more exciting when you're still full of strength and vigor. You can move your body faster, control your actions better, and get noticeably more pleasure.

There are a few other important things the perfect lover remembers before he starts sexual intercourse. I've devised a mnemonic to help you recall them during times of passion, when your brain may not exactly be functioning like Albert Einstein on the morning he thought of $E = mc^2$.

The magic word is CLIP.

C stands for Contraception. If you're screwing for love and/or pleasure, and not for the production of progeny, one or the other of you has to have something to thwart the enthusiasm of Nature for knocking girls up. A lot of girls take the pill these days, but not all, and some forget to take them regularly. As clinical as the question might sound, particularly in the middle of a romantic clinch, *ask*. If she isn't on the pill, have a condom handy. It might be unsophisticated to walk around with rubbers in your wallet, but it's totally naïve not to. Remember the Boy Scouts' motto—Be Prepared, Bring Prophylactics.

L stands for Location. The first time you make love to a girl, it may be better to stick to the traditional old bed. You won't be used to each other's sexual rhythms, and having a few good springs under you makes life easier. But if there are other exciting places to have it, give them a try. We all know about the shaggy rug in front of the blazing log fire, but all apartments and houses are full of other likely locations. Chairs, couches, carpets, balconies, hallways. Use your imagination and think of somewhere really unforgettable. A word of advice, though: if you're planning on having it in the bath, you'll need some extra waterproof lubrication, like Vaseline. Warm bathwater washes away vaginal juices and makes intercourse in the tub quite skiddy and uncomfortable.

I stands for Illumination. Perfect lovers generally don't make love in the dark, because they know that the sights of sex are just as stimulating as the sounds and the sensations. But turn off the overheads, because there's nothing more irritating than lying on your back with an 80-watt bulb glaring you in the eyes.

P is for Position. Give some consideration to the position in which you're going to be screwing. Don't always start off intercourse in the tried-and-tested missionary position (girl on back, man on top). Make your first move from an unexpected angle (more about these later) and see if you can elicit not only a gasp of satisfaction but one of delighted surprise.

Having settled all these points, and having turned her on to the shuddering point with your consummate love-play, get ready for insertion. If you're a goy, and you've got a foreskin, draw it back with your left hand, parting her vaginal lips with your knuckles. Then sli-i-ide your cock right in, until you hear her go "oohhff." It doesn't actually have to be "oohhff," anything similar will do. Would you believe "eerrrkk"?

It's at this point that many imperfect lovers demonstrate their imperfection. They start thrusting deep and heavy, their buttocks bouncing up and down like the Harlem Globetrotters after a baked bean supper. This kind of over-energetic behavior is not only *physically* miscalculated, it shows a misguided *emotional* attitude. You're not trying to have intercourse *to* her, you're having it *with* her. *Her* feelings and sensations are your most important consideration.

So tease her, coax her, guide her with your cock, lead her on, whip her up, and finally take her into a smooth, fluid finish.

Robert Chartham has a good word for the movement you should use during intercourse—"swing." *Swing* with your cock. It don't mean a thing if your dong don't swing.

Once you've pushed it in, draw it out again until only

the tip, the glans, is still inside her. Then gently and easily slide the glans in and out of her, resisting the temptation to plunge in deeper. The erotic effect of this restrained intercourse can be intense—both for you and for her. Remember that you've kept her waiting for this moment of insertion, and now you're teasing her some more. Her excitement is going to be whipped up even further.

So what do you do next? Keep up that held-back insertion of fireman's helmet alone, but with every third stroke, slide your cock right in. One-two-oohhff-one-two-eerrkk-one-two-oohhff-one-two, etc.

After a short spell of this, you'll be feeling like getting in there deeper yourself, and by the beard of Diocletian, so will she. So allow yourselves a longish period of what I call *striding*—long, even, measured strokes with your cock, regular and right up to the hilt.

You should find that as you're doing this, your tempo will naturally increase. Hold it back, brother, hold it back. After a while, the urge will get too stronge to resist, and then you can let go. But if you put your foot on the gas too soon, you'll find that you're straining to reach a climax when you should be letting it gradually build up in your balls to the point where even supreme control can't stop it.

But what if the opposite happens, and you find you're about to shoot long before either of you are really ready? First, slow the beat of your intercourse right down to a walking pace. Open her legs a little more, so that the sides of her vagina are not pressing so tightly on you, then adjust your position so that your penis is going *straight* into her, and not rubbing against the sides as you slide in and out.

Finally, you premature ejaculators, *think* about something else. How much you want for your next salary increase. Whether you should mow the front lawn tomorrow. Have you left the lights on at work. A friend of mine used to memorize whole pages of Ripley's *Believe It or Not*, and forestall premature ejaculations by mulling them over in his mind. Did you know, for instance, that an eighty-year-old Englishman used to sing himself to sleep every night?

You should be able to sense how close your bedmate is to orgasm by the squirming of her hips, the *possible* stiffening of her nipples, and her gasps for breath. All the time that you've been screwing her, you should have been kissing her, biting her, caressing and scratching her. As she nears her climax, you can turn your attention more and more to her bottom and vagina. Clutch her buttocks in your hands and, with every stroke of your cock, pull her even farther down on you. Pull the lips of her vulva even farther apart with the tips of your fingers, and thrust in deep. Massage her clitoris until she pants.

Above all, feel the *rhythm* you develop between you. This takes a lot of practice and experience, but once you've got a really rippling movement working between you, you'll both feel sensations that you didn't think possible. Although their actions are obviously exaggerated for display purposes, the couples who make love on stage in Stockholm's sex clubs are fascinating to watch for this flowing rhythmical fucking. Ulrich Geismar, who runs the most celebrated club, Chat Noir, told me that his performers didn't feel much during their acts, "but their technique is impeccable."

Exercise Eleven:
Take off your clothes, and if you can't get an erection spontaneously, masturbate yourself until you have. Tie a small rubber ball on elastic around the end of your cock, so that the ball dangles four inches above the floor. Now

put a record with a steady medium beat on the stereo. Relaxing your hips as much as possible, start a lovemaking motion in time to the record, so that the ball bounces regularly and evenly on the floor. It's not as easy as it sounds, but if you can master this exercise, and adopt the same "swing" in bed, your intercourse technique will be hard to beat.

I promised in Chapter Two to include some techniques for the smaller penis, and true to my word, here they are. These also apply if your wife or girl friend has had children, and has a less elastic vagina, so that sex with her, as the saying goes, is like throwing a banana up Broadway.

Despite the temptations to do the opposite, your smaller penis will give you more sensation in lovemaking if you keep your bedmate's legs flat on the bed, and eschew the old technique of tucking a pillow under her bottom. If she's prone, with her legs down, your penis will be sliding in at an angle, and subsequently there will be greater friction against the walls of her vagina.

As you near orgasm, you can actually get her to close her legs completely and make love to her with your legs outside. Her vagina will then be pressed together, and again the friction will be improved.

The "scissors" position is another good one for smaller cocks. Have your girl friend lie on her back with her legs raised. Lie on your side next to her, and insert your penis *sideways*. From this position, you can also push your finger into her anus, and massage the walls of her vagina against your cock as it goes in and out.

What about bigger cocks? I believe this response, from the editors of *Playboy* to a man who complained that girls were frightened of his eleven-inch pecker, is the classic answer:

"Wear dark, solid-colored suits. Never mix stripes with plaids. Make sure your socks match your trousers and keep your shoes shined. Turn out the light before you take off your clothes, then go gently into that good night. By the time she notices anything different (if she notices anything beyond her own pleasure), you will have hidden or disposed of most of the evidence."

During intercourse, apart from kissing, tickling, caressing, and actually screwing, you should be *talking* as well. It doesn't have to be much—something a little more verbose than President Nixon's resignation letter and a little less wordy than the Gettysburg Address, and infinitely more romantic than both.

Tell her how much she turns you on, what she's doing to you, what you're doing to her. Don't be afraid to use "four-letter" words to describe your feelings. They're earthy and unmistakable, and anything else sounds priggish. Any man who says: "Oh, Amanda, the way your labia minora grip on my glans is exquisite," just deserves to get kicked out of bed.

What positions should the perfect lover adopt during lovemaking? Should he change position in the middle of the proceedings, or stick with the one he started with?

It depends entirely on how the rhythms are going. Never break into a smooth-flowing session of in-and-outing just for the sake of trying another position. There are always natural breaks in the buildup toward orgasm, and those are the times to switch. I've never been in favor of the over-elaborate position, however; it's fine to try out a few variations during love-play and in the early stages of intercourse, but when you're developing those erotic sensations in earnest, you need to be as comfortable and relaxed as you possibly can be, and the chandelier is no place for that.

I've always thought that one of the best positions is face-to-face, with the woman on top. The cock goes in at a very stimulating angle, and the position has the advantage that by leaning forward or sitting back, the girl can control the depth of penetration. That means that she can actively help you bring her to orgasm. In this position, too, you can either lie there and let her do all the work if you're feeling too close to the edge of ejaculation, or you can thrust up into her as she bounces up and down on you if you want some extra arousing.

The "scissors," which I mentioned as a good technique for smaller penises, is another comfortable posture, and so is the "spoons," where you both lie on your sides facing the same way and you enter her vagina from the back. It's called spoons because you fit together like a couple of dessert spoons in a drawer. "Dog-coupling," where she gets up on all fours and you mount her from the back, can be very erotic, but also tiring. Reserve it for the position before the one in which you finally get your rocks off.

In essence, the perfect lover's position should always relate to what he is trying to do to excite his bedmate.

If you want to turn her on quickly with deep, rapid thrusts, lift up her legs and hook them over your shoulders, so that you can drive your penis into her to the maximum depth possible. If you just want to tickle and titillate her, raise your body up as far as you can while she lies flat on her back beneath you.

As your affair with any particular girl gets more advanced, what about those adventurous positions? Well, don't be afraid to try anything once, but don't be disappointed if positions like that don't *feel* as sexy as they *look*. It's quite an erotic sight to see a man holding a woman up in his arms, while screwing her at the same time. I know, because I've seen it done for a photograph.

But there isn't very much you can *do* in that position, because neither of you can move more than a few inches without falling over or doing yourselves a painful injury.

There are a couple of topics of intercourse etiquette I'm frequently asked about. Girls ask this one more than men: *Is it all right to have intercourse during my period?*

Now many men find the idea of this something of a turn-off. But a perfect lover doesn't. He knows that a lot of women feel especially sexy when they're menstruating, and he also knows he can make a considerable impression on a girl by showing that he doesn't care at all about her little "disability." I don't expect you to act like a Hell's Angel, and have cunnilingus with a girl at the wrong time of the month, but provided you are gentle and considerate, and don't mind a few stains on the sheets, intercourse can be just as satisfying on red letter days as any other.

Another question I'm asked is: *After intercourse, when should I take out my cock?* The answer I always give to that one is "sometime before breakfast." Seriously, it doesn't matter at all whether you remove it straight away or leave it there for a while. Some girls like to clean themselves up immediately afterward (perfect lovers always remember bedside tissues), while others prefer to lie in your arms, with your softening member still tucked inside them, feeling the warmth of companionship and the steady drip, drip of your combined juices making their way out.

If you're feeling really rampant, you may find that lying like this very rapidly gives you a second erection, and before you know where you are, you can be having it away again. This is pretty flattering for the girl, and another little memorable point in your favor. If you've done your penis exercises well, this trick shouldn't be too difficult for you.

It will help you in your role as a perfect lover to see that intercourse itself is not the be-all and end-all of a sexual relationship. Girls will appreciate your approach and attitude very much more if you see every part of what you are doing *to* them and *with* them as *equally important* in your time together. Going for a quiet stroll by the river is just as integral to your relationship as sliding your cock in. Remembering to telephone her one afternoon when you know she's alone or depressed can do you more good than ten brilliant fucks. The first few times you do considerate things like that, they may well be just technique, just string-pulling. But after a while you'll do them naturally, and that's when you'll be the kind of lover that women won't be able to resist.

Here's a twenty-one-year-old English girl talking about the way in which a man seduced her by a method like this:

"The first time I went out with Neil, he went at me like a bull in a china shop. After we'd been out dancing, I asked him in for a coffee, and almost before I knew where I was, he was all over me, kissing me and feeling me up and trying to get his hands into my pants. I was frightened and I was rather angry at the same time. I thought he was actually going to rape me. In the end we both got angry and he left. I was upset, because I did like him, but he seemed to be something of a sex maniac and that really put me off.

"About three weeks later, I was at home spending my birthday with my parents. I must admit I was rather fed-up and lonely. Then all of a sudden the telephone rang, and my mother answered it and said it was Neil. He was calling all the way from Scotland, where he'd gone away on business. But he'd remembered my birthday. All he did was ring up and say "Happy Birthday," but that was so thoughtful it did an awful lot to make up for how he'd behaved before.

"He called me again when he got back, and we went out for dinner. I think that first time must have taught him a lesson, because he was completely different. He wasn't all paws anymore. He was polite and nice, and asked me a lot of questions about me.

"When we went back to my place, I think the same thought was in both our minds. But he was obviously very anxious not to do the same thing again—which showed me that he *valued* me, that he was really interested in not putting me off again. He kissed me very tenderly, and we cuddled a lot, and then very gently he started undressing me. He said, "You can scream if you like," but of course I didn't. It was the first time I'd ever felt like undressing a man myself. I undid his trousers and his prick was very hard and big. He was stroking me all the time, and kissing me, and I began to feel very randy and weak at the knees. He was only half undressed, but I made him sit back on the couch, and I climbed on top of him and put his prick up me myself.

"I lifted myself up and down on him, faster and faster, until we were both panting and shouting out. I could actually feel his spunk go up me when he came off, and then I could feel it sliding down his prick again. Do you know something, it only occurred to me a long time afterward that he'd made me seduce myself."

The lesson to be learned from this true anecdote is that a man who constantly places the emphasis on sexual intercourse with a capital S is like a heavyweight boxer who shouts out, "I am now going to give you a left to the head." If a girl has any sense at all she will know that a man who finds her attractive would like to take her to bed. She doesn't need it spelled out.

Exercise Twelve:

Try and have sexual intercourse with someone today. Reread this chapter carefully before doing so, and adhere strictly to every suggestion and technique herein mentioned. After the lady's left, take notes on where you think you could have done better. Tomorrow, do it again and correct these errors.

If you do not currently have a bedmate, reread this chapter thoughtfully and then take a very cold bath.

EIGHT:

Hup-Two-Three-Four, and Other Sexual Exercises

Sex is the only physically strenuous activity that a man is expected to perform regularly—and well—without any prior training. Nobody suggests that a forty-year-old businessman, whose only exercise is a Sunday-morning walk with his dog, should be capable of running a 200-yard dash without gasping for breath. And yet that same man is expected to acquit himself honorably in bed, accomplishing something equally as hard on his heart, lungs, muscles, and circulation.

Sex is a matter of the flesh, and the flesh has to be in pretty fair condition before any of us can think about being perfect lovers. Apart from diet, which we've already discussed, the *only* way to get your body into good shape is to exercise—and exercise systematically.

"Systematically," I'm afraid, means every day.

If you value your performance and your appearance, set aside ten minutes each day for physical exercises. Not just any old ten minutes, but a very clear and specific ten minutes—just before your evening bath, for instance, or the moment when you wake up.

I have picked up these exercises, with the assistance of a professional instructor, to give you a good overall toning-up, and also to develop those parts of your body (your back, your legs, your lungs) that are most heavily used during intercourse.

If you already play some games or sports, like swimming, squash, golf, or tennis, then so much the better. But you can still benefit from daily work-outs like the ones that follow.

The exercises are laid out so that, over a period of one month, you can bring your physical condition gradually up to a reasonable level, and then maintain it at that level. Only willpower will enable you to keep at them—that and the knowledge that by the end of the course you will be ready to give any girl the time of her life in bed.

WEEK ONE

Exercise One
Start with your feet set apart and your arms raised, and then bend forward to touch your toes. Don't worry about keeping your legs straight. (Ten times)

Exercise Two
Lie on your back with your feet a little way apart. *Slowly* raise your head and shoulders clear of the floor. (Ten times)

Exercise Three
Lie on your stomach, with your hands under your thighs. Raise your head and chest slowly off the floor. (Ten times)

Exercise Four
Crouch down, with your hands touching the floor. Shoot your legs out backward and then return to a crouching position. (Eight times)

Exercise Five
Run in place, raising your knees as high as you can. Every fifteen steps, crouch down and touch the floor. (One hundred steps)

WEEK TWO

Exercise One
Start with your feet apart and your arms raised. Bend forward to touch the floor, keeping your knees straight, and press the floor twice when you touch it. (Fifteen times)

Exercise Two
Lie flat on your back on the floor, then raise yourself into full sitting position, keeping your heels flat on the floor. (Ten times)

Exercise Three
Lie flat on your face on the floor, then raise both your chest and your legs clear of the floor. (Twelve times)

Exercise Four
Lie on your face on the floor, and complete ten "push-ups," keeping your body and your legs straight.

Exercise Five
Run in place, raising your knees as high as you can,

crouching down every fifteen steps to touch the floor. (Two hundred steps)

WEEK THREE

Exercise One
Start with your feet apart and your arms raised. Bend down and touch your right foot, press, then touch the floor between your feet, press, then touch your left foot, press, and return to standing position. (Twenty times)

Exercise Two
Lie on your back flat on the floor. Lock your fingers behind your head, then raise yourself into full sitting position with fingers still locked. (Fifteen times)

Exercise Three
Push-ups. (Fifteen times)

Exercise Four
Lie on your back flat on the floor. Then lift your body up and touch your toes without bending your legs. (Ten times)

Exercise Five
Run in place, lifting your feet only six inches from the floor. Every fifteen steps, put your hands on your hips and bend your knees. (Two hundred steps)

WEEK FOUR

Exercise One
Start with your feet apart and your arms raised. Bend

down and touch your right foot, press twice, then touch the floor between your feet, press twice, then touch your left foot, press twice, and return to standing. (Twenty times)

Exercise Two

Lie on your stomach flat on the floor. Raise yourself on your arms with your body and legs straight, then quickly clap your hands before returning them to the floor and lowering yourself. (Twelve times)

Exercise Three

Lie on your stomach flat on the floor. Raise your chest off the floor with your arms wide apart, and as you raise yourself, lift your arms up behind you as high as you can. (Ten times)

Exercise Four

Lie on your back on the floor and touch your toes without bending your legs. (Twenty times)

Exercise Five

Run in place, raising your feet just four inches off the floor. Every fifteen steps, put your hands on your hips and bend your knees. (Two hundred steps)

Once you have reached Week Four, continue Week Four exercises every night for ten minutes. That will keep you in reasonable trim for nightly loving.

These exercises are not intended to develop you into a super-athlete or a rock-hard commando. All they will do is keep your body in reasonable working order for the stresses and strains of sex.

HOW TO BE THE PERFECT LOVER

When you think about it, it would be nice to whisper sweet nothings into your bedmate's ear after intercourse without panting like a Labrador, wouldn't it? Okay, gym shoes on.

NINE:

Up the Airy Mountain, Down the Rushy Glen

In those dear distant days when I worked for *Private*, the Swedish pornography magazine, a young woman sent me the following letter:

"I work in an office where I meet a lot of different people every day. Which is part of why I like my job so much. One day I was invited to lunch by a man who I found sexy and handsome, otherwise I never would have accepted. We had wine with the food, the atmosphere was romantic, candlelight and all the trimmings. I felt more and more attracted to him. To be honest, I was not only attracted to him, I was horny. I moved a bit closer to him and deliberately let my hand slide over his legs. From the way he looked at me I could see he was also turned on, and I knew he wanted me just as much as I wanted him. I desperately thought of what to do. The restaurant was crowded with people and my place was too far away. After some seconds I felt his hand caressing my thigh and I got completely wet between my legs. 'Why don't you go to the ladies, and I'll come after,' he said. 'Okay,' I said, and went.

"Fortunately, there were no other women there, so I just took off my panties and waited. A few minutes later he came in and we locked ourselves in the toilet. We didn't need any longer foreplay since we were both so damned excited. My lover folded me forward and drove his tool deep inside me. It was so good, I couldn't help moaning with pleasure, though I knew someone might hear us. When I had my orgasm I was screaming with passion, and just then I heard some knocks at the door. 'What the hell are you doing? Are you sick or what?' But my fucker kept on faster and faster, not paying any attention to the women outside the door. His orgasm was everlasting and all I could think of then was his hot sperm rushing into me.

"Afterward, we relaxed for a while, then opened the door and walked out past all the astonished women staring at us. Fortunately the bill was already paid, so we left the restaurant straight away. Intercourse during lunch hours—one of my very best and that I'd like to recommend."

How much of this little story was fantasy and how much of it was fact, I couldn't say. But whatever the truth of it, it was something that a real girl had dreamed about. It was either something she had actually done, or something she *wished* she'd done, with a perfect lover.

Where you make love, as far as becoming a memorable lover is concerned, is almost as important as *how* you make love. Exciting surroundings can turn even the most mundane screw into a Wonderful Experience.

In the chapter on intercourse, I mentioned the magic mnemonic CLIP—Contraception, Location, Illumination, Position. After contraception, *location* is easily the most important factor in your sexual exploits. You would do well to turn some active attention to finding some interesting spots for taking your lovemate.

The Great Outdoors is always better for interesting sex, but there are considerable hazards involved. Unless you're pretty sure that you're not going to run into mad bulls, wasps' nests, killer ants, termites, stinging nettles, outraged farmers, or giggling hikers, it's wiser not to take a girl out to the wilds on a first date. Sudden disaster is all right when your relationship is on a reasonably steady basis—running away from heifers with your pants around your ankles is all part of the fun—but earlier on in your affair *al fresco* sex should be well stage-managed.

Plan a likely spot well *beforehand*. It should be pretty, secluded, and sheltered. At the same time, it should be easy to reach from the road without an exhausting march. Girls are very easily put off by the idea of clambering through brambles and sweltering up rocky hills. Check the surrounding area for pathways, large animals, and low-flying planes. A friend of mine found what he thought was an ideal locale for hanky-panky in the countryside, only to be pestered for hours by hovering gliders. "They were worse than mosquitoes," he said. "You couldn't swat the gawkers."

If it's summer your first adventure into outdoor sex could begin as a picnic. Make it an impromptu picnic—a quickly bought loaf of French bread, a bottle of rough red wine, a hunk of cheese. If you let your would-be fieldmate prepare an elaborate repast, she'll be very offended if you don't eat it, and who wants to be chewing their way through an elaborate feast when they could be rolling free and naked through the grass, I ask?

Here's a description of just such a picnic from a nine-teen-year-old Scottish girl called Sarah.

"When Anthony called me up and said would I like to come for a picnic it didn't occur to me that anything like sex would happen, because somehow you don't think of it outdoors. But there are an awful lot of places in Scotland where you can make love in the rocks or the heather or somewhere like that.

"Anyway, he met me in his car, and it was a lovely afternoon, it was about the middle of August, and he had the roof of the car down. As I told you before, I liked Anthony a lot, and we'd been out together a few times, but we'd never taken it further than that. He had another girl friend called Eloise, and I was going out pretty steadily with John McLaren, so what there was between us had only been a little more than 'just good friends.'

"He stopped the car, at a small turn in the road, quite a woody place. We took the wine and sandwiches and we climbed straight up the hill by the road, alongside a little stream, until quite near the top we sat down. You could see all across the valley, and for quite a few miles north and south, but because we were in a kind of dip in the hill, no one could see us.

"We talked a lot and drank a lot, and then Anthony began to get very affectionate, and we started kissing and cuddling. I must admit I was getting quite turned on, but I did try and resist him a bit. But I was feeling so good, with the wine and the wind and the sun and the beautiful day and everything, it seemed silly not to enjoy it while it was there.

"He lifted my skirt, and tugged down my panties, and stroked me with his hands. I unzipped his trousers myself, because by that time I really wanted him, and I didn't care at all. I can remember opening his trousers and his john thomas sticking right out of them, with the end of it all wet.

"I lifted my bottom off the bracken for him, and he knelt down between my legs and pushed himself in, and the feeling of that, with the sun shining on my face and all, was something I won't forget. He held my bottom in his hands, and he pushed himself in and out of me so hard I thought I was going to faint with it. Then I felt something slide down the middle of my bottom, it was his come. He'd come, you know, and I was so far away with pleasure I hadn't even noticed.

"After that time, we met again every now and then, and just went to bed together. We never went out steady, because we didn't want to own each other that much. We just liked having sex together, and that's all there was to it. We tried to have it in places like that too, whenever we could—out of doors, in the fresh air."

Sarah was fortunate in having the Scottish countryside so close. But what happens if you live in the center of Chicago, and you have to battle your way through a ten-mile traffic jam to get within raping distance of a six-foot patch of grass? That's when the perfect lover has to come up with *inspiration*.

The first girl's account of a rapid romp in the ladies' lavatory is one crude but effective example. If you're really caught short for a location, or you want to set your pulses racing with some highly risky sex, you could try one of these (guaranteed true) suggestions.

Howard, the insurance salesman from Detroit: "My boss's wife Margie and I had had the hots for each other ever since I'd laid her at the firm's summer barbecue. But it was almost impossible to get near her after that, because my boss and I work so damn closely together. He knows when I finish work and he knows when I start.

"One morning Margie and I both stepped into the elevator together, just us two. We kissed, and then before I really thought about it, I pressed the emergency switch between floors. I said to her: 'It's now or never,' and I flipped up her dress, pulled her pants to one side, got out my cock and screwed her from the back, while she held on to the hand rail and just whimpered.

"It took the engineers only ten minutes to get us out of there. I'm surprised no one realized what had been going on, because the whole elevator reeked of sex. We walked out of there with our knees trembling and our faces scarlet, but I'm never going to forget it, and neither will she."

Terence, young lawyer from Boston: "I went to the Cape to spend the weekend with my girl friend Carole's parents. They wouldn't let us share a bedroom, of course, and so by Sunday afternoon we were pretty frustrated. In the end, when the whole family were sitting around the fire snoozing after lunch, we tiptoed our way into the music room, and got into a corner. Carole pulled her jeans down, and I pulled my pants down, and we tried to get it on standing up.

"We'd just started to get going, and I had my prick right up inside her when we heard Carole's elderly aunt coming down the corridor. We shuffled over, still joined together, and hid behind the door. The aunt came in and sat down at the piano and started to play. She played *Eine Kleine Nachtmusik*, which must last for at least fifteen minutes. And all the time we were standing behind the door, very very quietly fucking.

"In the end, the aunt got up and went out. I shut and locked the door behind her, laid Carole down on the carpet, and we finished making love in about five seconds flat. Our hearts were thumping so fast that we both had a tremendous climax, and Carole had to bite my hand to stop herself from crying out."

The best places for sex of this kind are the places where no one else thinks sex is possible or plausible. Cornfields are corny—if you see a couple wandering hand in hand into the middle of a barley crop, you know for sure they're not inspectors from the Department of Agriculture. But if you see a couple getting into an elevator, or walking into a room that manifestly isn't a bedroom, or climbing the stairs that lead to the roof of an office building, or going out of the first exit door in an apartment building, then illicit intercourse isn't exactly the first thing that enters your mind.

When, as a perfect lover, you want to try out an unlikely locale, think of what you're doing from the *onlooker's* point of view, and choose the unlikeliest; you could join the "sky-high" club of people who have made love on scheduled air flights, for instance. Xaviera Hollander, the celebrated former call-girl, recently recommended this method for aerial intercourse.

"I suggest you do it the way I did on my way to South Africa once, stretched out on a couple of seats with the arm dividers removed. That was a bit cramped, but we did it lying one behind the other barely covered by a thin blanket. But at least it was more comfortable than having it vertically in the airplane's bathroom."

Porno king Berth Milton has another idea: "What about a cemetery on a black, windy night? Many women shudder in exalted fright, with small wish-fantasies of rape." That's translated from the Swedish, but you get the gist of it.

Public parks, beaches, railway embankments, balconies—keep your eyes and your notebook open, and you should be able to collect a fair number of likely localities for love. The perfect lover is an *original* lover, and as the old Chinese saying goes: "Only once, out in the fields or by the side of the road, surrounded by the peace of Nature, is worth as much as a thousand times in bed."

Exercise Thirteen:

Make a short list of twelve good places, apart from the bedroom, for making love. Six of them should be the kind of spot where you won't be disturbed, no matter how long you stay or how extravagant your lovemaking. The other six should be "hot spots," where it's possible to make love, but where there's a risk of being caught out.

A young businessman I know regularly plans "outings" with his wife, to excite and surprise her. One of his most successful ideas was to hire a prostitute's bedroom, complete with mirrors and sado-masochistic equipment, where he and his spouse spent an extremely erotic evening. "The only setback was that the phone kept ringing, and gruff men would keep asking how much a 'service' was," he told me.

The principal point to remember is that sex outside the bedroom should be—or at least *appear* to be—spontaneous. A girl may be very excited by the idea of having a quickie in the office stockroom, but if she feels you've planned it for weeks in advance, then much of the enjoyment will go out of it for her. She wants to feel that you need her sexually so much that you just can't wait, no matter what the dangers.

I've saved for last one of my favorite stories of seduction in unusual places. I have only the word of the man who claims to have done it that it's true, but I took the trouble to visit the location with a stopwatch and I must admit that it's feasible.

To the west of Stockholm lies the island of Drottningholm, where the summer palace traditionally occupied by the kings of Sweden is located. (I deliberately haven't called it a royal palace, because like everything else in Sweden it's owned by the state.) On the ground floor of this palace is a very unusual bedroom, with a massive four-poster bed resting in a large alcove.

Every few minutes, a party of sightseers, accompanied by a guide, walks through this bedroom on a tour of the principal palace chambers. There is probably, at most, an eight-minute gap between parties.

Ingemar K., the young computer salesman who told me the story, took his girl friend Khristine to Drottningholm, and together they joined one of the tours. He had planned everything well in advance, but he only suggested it to Khristine as they began to walk around.

"Two or three rooms before we got to the bedroom, I told the guide that Khristine needed some fresh air, and we left the party as though we were on our way out," said Ingemar. "We went straight to the bedroom, into the alcove, pulled down our pants, jumped on the bed and had the quickest, most panicky fuck I've had in my life. I was nearly reaching a climax when we heard the party come shuffling into the room next door—the wooden floors make a peculiar squeaking there, and they were easy to hear.

"Khristine lost her nerve and sprang up, and I ejaculated all over this priceless bedspread. I straightened the bed as quickly as I could, and we got out of the room just as the party was turning the doorhandle to come in."

HOW TO BE THE PERFECT LOVER

Full marks for originality, full marks for timing, and write out one hundred times "I shall not come on historic bedspreads."

TEN:

Manners Makyth Woman

All right, so you know all about opening doors for ladies, walking on the outside of the sidewalk so that their clothes won't get splashed by passing vehicles, standing up when they enter the room, helping them put their coats on and helping them take them off.

But what do you know about *sexual* manners?

Girls, despite their liberation and their independence, still like to feel *looked after* when it comes to sex, and that's what erotic etiquette is all about.

I've mentioned some major points of sexual politeness already—like not forcing a girl to fellate you, and making sure that you show your appreciation after making love. But there are quite a few other little ways in which the perfect lover can show his consideration.

If you've spent a whole day with a girl, and you're coming back to your apartment to make love, always offer her a shower or bath. Both of you will appreciate being really clean before hitting the hay. If you've been dating her for quite a while, make an effort to get to know which deodorant, perfume, and foundation makeup she uses (a quick reconnaissance of the vanity in her apartment is usually enough), and have them ready for her in the bathroom. Provide an extra toothbrush.

When she gets into bed, naked in front of you, *don't* make critical remarks about her, no matter how innocuous you may think they are. Her eyes may look smaller without lashes, but don't say so. She may have marks on her skin from bra and panties, but don't point it out. And for God's sake don't come blurting out with, "Shit, I've never seen breasts like *that* before."

Particularly if it's the first time she's gone to bed with you, she'll be nervous, unsure of herself, and anything you can do to reassure her will win you extra marks. Not being critical is not enough—be flattering and obviously delighted with her. She's given you the greatest present she knows how to give—don't accept it as though it's another pair of socks from Aunt Minnie.

Compliment her all the time you're making love. A few whispers of "Oh, you're beautiful" are always welcome. She may think you're bullshitting her, but leave that decision to her. Girls will always prefer to give you the benefit of the doubt when you're dishing out praise.

During sex give her the chance to take the initiative if she wants to. You don't need to keep on proving your masculinity and your dominance when you're both bare-ass naked, and sometimes it's *fun* to be raped by a woman. If she's eager to suck you, or climb on top of you, let her do it. But when you're on top of *her*, don't forget the whiskery adage that "a gentleman takes the weight on his elbows." It may be dated, but countless girls have told me that their boyfriends have crushed them remorselessly into the mattress.

After sex, offer her tissues to mop herself with, and also a drink. Screwing, particularly in today's air-conditioned apartments, is thirsty work, and there is nothing like a chilled white wine after the loving's over.

Another thing, after sex, stay sexy. I've known so many women who have complained that the minute their husbands or boyfriends have shot their bolt, their minds immediately go back to day-to-day routine male topics, and they start burbling on about politics or how their Mustang needs new gaskets (no reflection on the Ford Motor Company there).

Sexual pundits have been trying to tell us for so long that sex is just an ordinary old appetite, like eating a meal or quaffing a beer, but it's damn well not, and it never will be. A girl wants more than a "thank you" and a Diner's Club card when it's over.

Remember something else: if you've got a girl into bed once, that doesn't give you droit de seigneur over her for ever after. Until your sexual relationship is very well developed, and even then, she needs and deserves to be wooed and seduced every time you make love. She may give you the feeling that it's not necessary, but that's only because she feels secure with you. It's a sign that you're doing the right thing—not that you should stop doing it.

As far as sexual manners *outside* the bedroom are concerned, a little imagination stretches a long way. Don't screw and tell. You may have had the most mind-blowing night of erotic love in your whole life, but try and keep it to yourself. Sexual gossip has a nasty habit of coming back to the gossiper on an uncatchable curve. You can be as proud and smug as you like, but just let other people draw their own conclusions (they usually will).

A friend of mine in Milwaukee once spent almost half an hour at a cocktail party describing, in the lascivious detail for which he had a particular bent, the sexual gymnastics of his latest girl friend. The middle-aged man in whom he was confiding all these intimate particulars listened quietly and sagely, and then said gently: "I don't think you'd better go on. There are *some* things a father shouldn't know about his daughter, wouldn't you agree?"

If you're fond of a girl, show it. That doesn't mean you have to snuffle around her all the time, treating her as though she's a ray of sunshine out of the asshole of Heaven. Just be natural, normal, and affectionate. Telephone her at surprise times to tell her you think she's terrific. Take her flowers (*never* send them by messenger), but don't overdo it. Eight dozen red roses will put you strictly into the Fred Astaire class.

The greatest compliment you can pay to any girl is to show her simply that you see her as a woman, and that you respect her womanhood. And a big part of respecting her womanhood is respecting your own manhood. You will have much more enjoyable sex relationships if you show that you *expect* her to be feminine and alluring and lovely, and keep her on her toes.

My good friend Rosalind Erskine, who wrote that scandalous book of schoolgirl courtesanship, *The Passion Flower Hotel,* once humorously described for me the difference between stylish manners and self-abasement:

"Take the girl who gets stood up for a date," she explained. "She waits in the Savoy Bar, or under the clock at Waterloo. She waits for an hour and a quarter and then goes home in a fury. The ordinary man *must* send bunches of flowers and boxes of chocolates, must abase himself and beg forgiveness, even though he was suddenly sent to Glasgow on secret government business, was in an aircrash, saved six babies from drowning in a storm off Brighton Pier, and went to Buckingham Palace to be invested with his George Cross. The stylish man simply allows himself to be seen three days later walking with a slight, glamorous limp. The girl's heart jumps. What has happened? Oh, nothing. Not worth talking about. The merest trifle. The car spun off the road. They were very good at the hospital. Of course it was lonely. One had hoped for a visitor, a message. If she had cared at all . . ."

Exaggeratedly caddish, yes. But Rosalind has neatly summed up the difference between behaving like a slave and behaving like an independent man who really appreciates women. No matter what you think, no girl wants you to be anything but *yourself*, and you will very rapidly lose her respect if you try to be anything else in the mistaken hope that she will like you more. The ultimate in good sexual manners is to be just who you are—considerate, appreciative, and polite maybe—but you and only you.

Girls like flattery, and they're impressed by clever, sophisticated talk. But they have an uncanny ability to see through boasting and bullshit, and they remember everything you've said with supernatural clarity, long after you've forgotten it. It's not only good manners to tell a semblance of the truth—it can also save you a lot of sweat.

Now we come to the ticklish point of sexual etiquette. Suppose a certain lover forgot that vital "C" in CLIP. She wasn't on the pill, but the night was hot and romantic, and he'd left his rubbers at home, in his green plaid jacket with the torn lining. Intercourse occurred. Her next period *didn't* occur. Suddenly, he was about to become a father.

The way I look at this problem is this (and I've been through it myself, so I'm talking from grizzled experience). Although it's an unwise lover who doesn't use a contraceptive, it's also a foolish girl who lets herself be screwed by an unmackintoshed man. It takes two to procreate, and the responsibility rests on *both* their heated heads. Each should feel guilty, but not totally guilty.

The perfect lover, if he unwittingly finds himself with a knocked-up girl friend on his hands, does not promptly abandon ship and pretend it's nothing to do with him. He makes sure the girl goes to the clinic *quickly* for a pregnancy test, and if it proves positive, he lays things on the line.

If she wants to keep the baby, but he doesn't want to be a husband or father, he tells her quite clearly where he stands. He offers to help with money, but he makes no formal promise or written commitment, neither does he admit in writing that he is the father. These last points might sound callous, but they're for the man's own legal protection.

If she'd rather have an abortion, he offers to go halves on the cost. If she hasn't got her half, he lends it to her. It's far more important that she have the abortion as early in her pregnancy as possible than haggle over who's going to pay what to whom and when. If she has any pride, she'll pay him back eventually.

He takes her to the abortion clinic, and stays with her afterward, or arranges for one of her friends to stay with her. Some girls are deeply emotionally upset by abortion, and comfort and support are more than welcome. Only when the bother has died down does he assess what's happened to their feelings for each other. The perfect lover isn't unduly surprised if the relationship from henceforth is at an end.

The only thing I can add to this glum but salutary discussion is that, these days, it should never happen. I know that condoms are tedious and unromantic, but the lover who takes the trouble to sheath his sword is the lover who goes on vanquishing ladies long after the others have petered out.

That sounds like a commercial, and maybe it is.

ELEVEN:
A Man and Some Women

Girls are better than lampreys, because unlike lampreys you can never have too many of them. Not, that is, if you're a perfect and perfectly *organized* lover.

The joy of running two or three or more affairs at the same time is that when you grow bored with Liza's enormous knockers, or Christine's talk about leftist politics, or Andrea's ginger pubic hair, you can always go and spend a night with Edwina, and revel in her globe-shattering talent for fellatio.

Before the ever-sensitive voice of Women's Liberation shrieks stridently in protest, I am not necessarily suggesting that one woman is not enough for one man. All I am saying is that when you don't have marriage or a steady relationship in mind, and you are simply out to enjoy yourself, there is no reason why you should remain ever faithful, ever true to a single girl.

You're training to be a perfect lover, and you can't train without practice. With several simultaneous affairs on the run, you will have an unparalleled opportunity to compare the personalities, the sexual predilections, and the sexual performances of the various girls you're dating. And you'll also be able to compare your own ratings with different types of female companions.

What you learn from your mistakes with one girl you can test out on another. If Bedmate #1 complains about your rough-cut sexual techniques, you can try smoothing them out with Bedmate #2. That means you'll have a chance to give your newly polished intercourse an experimental dry-run, without making it obvious to #1 that you're giving in to her just because she's complained. And if any further refinements are required, you can always give them a whirl with Bedmate #3.

Having more than one mistress will keep you sexually alert, bright-eyed, and bushy-tailed, and it will also give you more erotic experience in a far shorter time than could ever have been possible with a single girl. Remember, though, that women can be like Indian clubs: if you juggle too many of them too clumsily, they're all liable to drop on your head at once. Very hard.

If you're planning on going into the multistory love-affair business, your most vital piece of equipment is one of those diaries in which you can see the whole year at a glance. Whenever you make a date, or whenever any of your girl friends makes a single relevant move, *write it down at once*. There is no watertight way of ensuring that one Saturday afternoon, when you're dallying in bed with Bridget, the hot-tempered Lola won't suddenly decide to pay you an unannounced visit, but if you're willing to take that kind of risk, the more obvious dangers can be eliminated by thoughtful, strategic organization.

An Irish friend of mine who was notorious for his complex love-life used to call his study "the War Room." He kept on the wall a large-scale map of the city, with colored pins representing different girls and their last-known locations. He was also sensible enough to keep a memory-jogger: a notebook in which he wrote down the salient points of the last conversation he had had with any particular girl, along with a list of general information. This, snatched straight from his actual book, is an example:

"Susan P. Age: 21. Hair: Brown. Eyes: Blue. Statistics: ca 36-25-37. Occupation: PR Assistant. Home Address: 23a, Somewhere Gardens, Tel: 0000. Work Address: Bligh & Co., Bounty Buildings. Tel: 0000.

"Where we met: Sibylla's Discotheque, January 20, 1974. What happened: Asked her for dance, then out to pub in Jermyn Street for drinks, then back to her place for nightcap, then bed. Personal information gleaned: Spends weeks in city, weekends at home in Bedfordshire with stockbroker family. Middle-class, educated at Something College, expecting £17,500 legacy at age 25. Wants to travel before settling down, likes the idea of 'rape-like' violent sex. Likes French food, ballet, and antique porcelain.

"Last time we met: May 4, 1975. Went to Chez Victor for Provençal tripe. Then bed. Talked about: Watergate, rape, where she wanted to go for summer holiday.

"Special peculiarities: Calls my cock 'Fido.'"

Depending on how dangerous a love-life you wish to lead, it is probably better to select your stable of bedmates from very different backgrounds and different parts of the city in which you live. Even this sort of precaution, however, cannot guarantee that the long arm of coincidence will not find you out. I once discovered by accident that my secretary's roommate had been a close friend of a former girl friend of mine—even though this was in London, and I had met my girl friend in the Far East.

Your attention to detail, however, will be your strongest ally in your multifarious misdeeds. Never run even remotely unnecessary risks. Don't take different girls to the same restaurants or clubs. The night that she's not with you, Bedmate #2 might suggest to another escort of hers that they drop in to "a great little spot I know," and there you'll be, cheek-to-cheek and crimson-eared, with Bedmate #5.

If you are spotted by #2 while waiting in your car at the traffic lights with #5, *don't* pretend that you haven't seen her. Smile and wave and pray to the Lord that the lights will change. You can always tell both of them that the other is a friend of your sister. Only guilty behavior will give you away.

When you are found out, *don't* deprecate the girl you were discovered with. Don't try and say: "Oh *her,* she's just a boring old hag I promised my mother I'd take out." Unless your taste in girl friends is singularly unappealing, she won't have looked like a boring old hag. Say something more on the lines of: "Oh yes, that was Jenny. I've known her for ages. She's rather fun. We went for a drink together."

If you want to keep your affairs going, even after discovery, grit your teeth and keep playing the game. But whatever you do, don't let any of your girl friends meet any other of your girl friends. Once they start comparing notes about you, you are definitely sunk. There is a sisterhood between women in the same plight that is stronger and more irresistible than any temptation you can come up with. If you've ever commiserated with a man friend who's had trouble with a girl you both know, then you'll realize exactly what I mean.

Girls are not so much jealous of each other, but jealous of the attention that you give to other girls. If they both realize they're in the same boat, they'll probably go off together the best of friends, leaving you without two of your prime partners.

But if it happens, shrug and carry on. The perfect lover does not bear a grudge. As you'll see later, the art of sexual supremacy depends almost as much on getting *out* of relationships gracefully as it does on getting *into* them.

Personal tidiness and organization are also important factors in running several affairs at once. Did Joanna leave a barrette in the bathroom the last time she was staying the night with you? Did Molly lend you a book with her name in the front? Are there any of the classic long blond hairs around (check woolens in particular)?

I suggest you keep in your apartment a "panic box"— that is, a locked box in which you can quickly sling and shut away all incriminating evidence. It's worth keeping one in your car too, because girls have an extraordinary weakness for leaving sunglasses, scarves, cardigans, gloves, cigarette lighters, and other debris in other people's automobiles. My Irish friend claimed he charged a fine for every article left in his car, which amounted to enough to buy him thirty pints of Guinness on his thirtieth birthday.

Never give any girl a key to your place. Apart from the fact that she might wander in blithely at an embarrassing moment, jilted girls have a strange habit of becoming hysterical. There was a report in the newspapers recently about a girl who went to her boyfriend's apartment and scratched every one of his 1,000 long-playing records, just for spite. Don't ever give any girl friend of yours the opportunity to do something like that, because one day she just might. Hell hath no fury, etc.

Then there's the question of the telephone. I have a particular phobia about the telephone. Nobody ever calls me up to give me good news, or if they do, they call at the most embarrassing time.

You can't really do anything constructive about the telephone, apart from ripping it out of the wall. If it rings when you're with one girl, and you strongly suspect it's another girl, all you can do is answer it. Stay calm, don't try to be evasive, and don't lose your temper. If your unwelcome caller asks you things like: "Do you love me?" answer, "Fantastically." If she says, "Well, say it then," answer, "I just did," and hope she won't try and make a meal out of it. It's all part of the risk, I'm afraid.

When you're dating two or three girls at one time, you will find yourself having to lie occasionally—or at least having to make elaborate and not wholly accurate excuses. But for God's sake don't get carried away and start Bunburying (Algernon, a character in Oscar Wilde's *Importance of Being Earnest,* invented an invalid friend called Bunbury, whom he could "visit" at convenient moments). Keep your excuses as near to the truth as possible: it makes them easier to substantiate and, more important, easier to remember.

The most delicate excuse you'll ever have to make is why you don't feel very horny tonight.

The necessity to produce an erection, and what's more, an ejaculation, is the plague of male philanderers. That very morning you may well have been in the tigerish arms of Trixie, whose near-nymphomaniac appetites have drained you both spiritually and physically. Suddenly you're faced with the equally voracious Victoria, who is wondering out loud why Fido is looking hangdog this evening.

Surely you're not going to have to come out with the

lame old excuse of the frigid housewife: "Not tonight, darling, I'm too tired"?

If you've been doing your exercises properly, and eating properly, and trying to get in as much sleep as you can, you shouldn't be in too much of a fix. One solution, used by a printing executive I know, with at least 80 percent claimed success, is to have some very pornographic magazines in the apartment, excuse yourself for five minutes, and pore over them in the hope of regaining some of your faded fruitiness.

When even this kind of emergency measure doesn't work, simply admit that you can't handle it, and use the methods described earlier in this book to give her the best arousal you can. If she asks you whether there's someone else, all you can reply is: "What do you think?"

Here's a true anecdote from a journalist friend who found himself in this very position.

"The night before, I'd been with Madeleine. I hadn't seen Madeleine for a month, because she'd been away, and when she came back, it was obvious she hadn't been laid the whole time. She didn't even want to be taken out, she just wanted to go straight to bed and screw. I was still in the living room pouring out a drink when she appeared at the bathroom door stark naked, with her nipples sticking up like typewriter keys.

" 'Look,' she said, 'I've shaved off all my pubic hair.' And she had, too. I think it was the horniest thing I'd ever seen. She was absolutely bare down there, except for a bit of talcum powder, and you could see everything she had. Then to make matters worse she came and climbed on top of me and pulled her cunt open with her fingers to show me what it looked like. I had a hard-on to end all hard-ons.

"We got into bed at about seven o'clock, and I think we had it away six times during the night. I dozed off for about half an hour at around five o'clock, but I woke up to find Madeleine halfway down the bed with her mouth around my prick, trying to get me going again. By the time it came to morning, I was totally, utterly knocked out.

"Then I had to go to work, and there were endless editions all morning and half the afternoon. By the time I got home, I was urped out. And who should be there, waiting outside the door, but Charlie—Charlotte. She'd been kicked out of her place, and wanted to know if she could spend the night.

"What could I say? I mean Charlie is actually supposed to be the Number One girl. So I said yes, and when I opened the door I whipped through the apartment like a maniac, checking that Madeleine hadn't left anything around. She hadn't, fortunately. Charlie and I had a couple of Scotches, and then she started getting all worked up. I can tell you, screwing was about the last thing I felt like doing.

"I was slumped out there on the couch, and Charlie took my clothes off and worked away for about fifteen minutes to get some sort of response, and then she said: 'What's the matter, have you lost interest in me?' I said of course I hadn't, I was just a bit whacked. She sat back and looked a bit suspicious and a bit disappointed, and I really started to feel desperate.

"I went to the bathroom for a leak and a wash, and what should I see there but my trusty Gillette razor, cram full of Madeleine's pubic hair. I rinsed it away as quickly as I could, and then suddenly I thought of something. I went back to the living room and said to Charlie: 'Would you let me do anything I wanted with you?' She said: 'Yes, within reason.'

"So I told her not to say a word, and I brought a basin of water and some shaving lotion into the living room, and I lifted up her skirt and took down her pants. Then I rubbed her pubic hair all over with lotion, and I shaved her. By the time I had finished doing that, I was as hard as a stick of rock, and she was really juicy. We had it away on the couch right there and then—and do you know what I think really turned me on was that there were two girls walking around with no pubic hair, just to attract me, and neither of them knew about the other."

Male chauvinist pig—what?

Those are some of the physical and practical aspects of having sex with more than one girl at once, but what about the emotional problems?

Suppose you're actually in love. It is, of course, quite possible for one man to be almost equally in love with two (or even more) girls at the same time. But if you're really *in love*, rather than just playing the field, the moment will inexorably arrive when you have to make up your mind which of the women you want. Deceiving two women you respect will eventually take its toll on your health and morale.

I'm not going to pretend that decisions like this are easy—either for you or for the girls you love. But in the long run, the least painful way is to make a decision, kill the relationship you feel you have to end, and forget about it. Forgetting takes time, but as Christopher Logue once remarked in a poem of his: "The day will come when I do not think about her, even once."

If you're *not* in love, *your* emotional problems will be

fewer, but you may have to tread more delicately around the feelings of your several girl friends. If you don't love them, then for God's sake don't pretend that you do. Be pleasant, affectionate, and sexually passionate, but don't ever profess that you feel an emotion that you don't. You will hurt more people than you need, and that is not what being a perfect lover is all about. There should be no necessity to raise false hopes in a girl's eager young breast—not if you are a good enough bedmate and companion yourself.

What if your various bedmates discover each other's existence and tell you that they don't mind? That they'd rather go on sharing you with someone else than give you up?

It does happen, but I don't think the men to whom it happens are any happier in their sexual relationships because of it. There are too many spoken or unspoken questions from their girl friends for comfort. ("Am I as good in bed as she is?" "Does she do *this* to you?" "Can she cook/kiss/mend your socks as well as I can?")

No—enjoy your secret sultanate as long as you can, but don't hang on too long after the game is up. One notorious figure of history hung on too long, and look what happened to him. There should be nothing of Richard Nixon in the perfect lover.

Expletive, as they say, deleted.

TWELVE:

One into Two Will Go!

Since I always like to end my chapters on a sober and socially responsible note, there's one little tidbit I left out of the last one. Two girls in one bed.

The mind, not to mention the penis, boggles.

There are occasions in the life of a perfect lover when he is presented with the opportunity to share his princely sack with more than one girl. My advice to you, in all seriousness, is that when such a chance arises, you should take it. It doesn't happen often, but when it does, it's worth more than a year's free supply of Gravy Train, dog bowl included.

The Absolute Number One male fantasy of all time, which merits an entry in *The Best*, is to have twin sisters, preferably blonde and with very large tits, in the same bed at the same time. Oh yes, and they should both be nymphomaniacs with some lesbian leanings.

Since the world is not completely packed with twin blonde sisters with very large tits, the chances of this happening to the average American or European lover are about 1:107,000,000. But if you're prepared to accept the Number Two fantasy, which is two sisters, non-twins, in the same bed, or the Number Three fantasy, which is two girls, unrelated, in the same bed, then the odds are very much more in your favor.

It's not easy to engineer the kind of situation in which two girls will come to bed with you. It depends very much on the girls and their relationship with each other. It's also the kind of sexual incident that happens spontaneously during a party or after an evening's friendly drinking. But there's no harm in trying to set the scene for such antics, even if they don't lead you anywhere.

Exercise Fourteen:
Invite two girl friends, or your principal girl friend and a very close friend of hers, around for the evening. Have plenty of booze and light snacks at hand. Talk, play records, enjoy yourselves until it's very late. It's important that it should be very late, so there's less of an excuse for the girls to go home. If both girls stay for the night, broach the subject with your principal girl friend of the other girl sharing your bed with you both. "Have you ever thought what it would be like to have three people in one bed . . ." If she is definitely and positively frosty about it, drop it and forget it. You've had a nice evening, anyway. If she shows some interest, suggest that she goes and chats to her friend. This approach is always much better—it seems much less lecherous if one girl can ask the other.

There are a great many "ifs" in this exercise. But I have based it on two experiences that happened to girls I knew personally, and in each case this was almost exactly how it took place.

Most girls are extremely curious about lesbianism—one girl I knew was absolutely fascinated by other girls' breasts—and the opportunity to try it out can strongly arouse them. With a man present (you), the guilt of feeling homosexual is almost completely removed.

HOW TO BE THE PERFECT LOVER

Case history from Elinor, a twenty-three-year-old Swedish girl:

"I cannot remember very well how it happened that we all got into the one bed. I did not know Stig, the boy, very well. But I had known Birgit ever since we were at school. We were very good friends but of course not lesbians.

"My boyfriend was away for a college examination, and Stig and Birgit asked me to have an evening meal with them. We had a lot of wine, and we watched television, and then Stig and Birgit said they were going to bed. Stig had been very friendly to me all the evening, putting his arms around me and things like that. Birgit made up a bed for me in the living room, but after we had all washed and got ready for sleep, she came in to see me. She was completely naked, and I was staring at her breasts and her body, I suppose because I was curious. But I also found it aroused me a little bit.

"Birgit said very simply that it would be nice, and she would like it, if I came into their bed with them. I remember I went red. But in the end I said that I would. I think I was quite excited by the idea.

"I went into the bedroom and Stig was lying there naked in the lamplight. His tool was up, and I can remember how it bobbed slowly up and down by itself. I took off my blouse, which I had been going to wear to bed, but I left my panties on. Then I got on the bed next to Stig.

Birgit also got on to the bed, and started kissing Stig and fondling his chest and arms. Then she put her hand down and fondled his balls. I could not help looking. I felt a very strange feeling, watching this, but it made me very aroused indeed.

"Suddenly Birgit knelt and began to suck Stig's tool. I could actually see the end of it disappear into her lips. I

120

leaned over and kissed Stig on the mouth, and he kissed me back and fondled my breasts, and after that I knew that almost anything could happen.

"I moved down Stig's body with kisses, kissing his chest and his tummy, and then Birgit and I kissed and sucked his tool together. We took it in turns to lick and suck the end, and we kissed each other with his tool in between our mouths.

"Then Birgit moved away and left me sucking Stig's tool by myself. She pulled down my panties and began to kiss my legs and thighs, and then all of a sudden I could feel her tongue between my legs, on my pussy. I can remember I reached down and stroked her long hair and touched her face and even her tongue where it was actually licking me.

"We went on and on like this for hours. I licked Birgit myself. I can remember thinking *I am licking a woman's pussy*, but it tasted beautiful and I felt so much love for Birgit that I knew it must be all right. The end was fantastic. Stig finally came, right into my mouth when I was sucking him, and I kissed Birgit straight away, and let all the come flow into her mouth.

"I know I'm not a lesbian. I know that, for certain. What I like about three people in one bed is that one can help the other two, by kissing them and licking them at times when it would not usually be possible, and also it is exciting when you are a couple to have someone else watching you."

If such an incident ever happens, fortuitously, to you, don't expect it ever to happen again—not with the same girls, anyway. One orgiastic evening is one thing, but as Birgit herself later told me: "I did enjoy it, but there was no doubt I was a little bit jealous of seeing Stig making love with Elinor." In other words, threesomes are not the basis of sound, long-lasting relationships.

What about the opposite—two or more men and one girl?

This is another very potent fantasy, if its constant appearance in porno magazines is anything to go by. I quote verbatim the text from a full-color photo-story in *Fifteen*, a magazine which announces on its cover: "This is a new pornographic magazine for you who like very young girls. You will see them in tough orgies with plenty of variations. We hope you will get really randy from reading *Fifteen*." That is to say, it's not exactly *The Saturday Evening Post*.

Here's the text:

"This is Ingrid, a Swedish schoolgirl of the merry sort. Nobody at her school knows what she is up to in her break. But *Fifteen*, which hears and sees everything, here gives a full account of her secretive lunch break.

"Ingrid has an affair with three older men, semi-drunkards, who hang out in a flat opposite her school. There she gets fucked every day by every way in the book, and that gives her indescribable satisfaction.

"On the day *Fifteen*'s camera was present, the drill started by all three men taking Ingrid at once. Unusually hard obviously, for she bleated like a little lamb throughout. One of the men rather quickly got into her mouth which wasn't big enough by half, and half her face was covered in sperm, as you can see for yourself in the pictures.

"Then they shaved little Ingrid, who was so worked up by this that she could not contain her urine but peed straight out to the delight of all concerned.

"Now an even more violent round started, and when one of the men temporarily lost his hard, Ingrid posed before him in the most shameful manner, like here for instance with a necklace stuck up her cunt. Something which always works in this strange company.

"In this last picture you can see Ingrid swallow a shot approaching a pint."

I've quoted this questionable text because it so clearly illustrates the underlying compulsions in this particular fantasy. One of the strongest ingredients is the total subjection of the girl—she becomes nothing more than a sexual receptacle for any man who cares to use her.

If you, as a perfect lover, ever get the chance to involve yourself in a "gang-bang" orgy like this one, there are one or two important points to remember. First, there are *never* any "gang-bang orgies" like this one. *Fifteen*'s fictitious Ingrid had no real personality and behaved simply as a machine; and the men, her "semi-drunkard" lovers, were nothing more than anonymous penises, with no true emotional existence.

When you get your chance, you will find that the girl is a real girl with real feelings, and that the other man or men with whom you are sharing her are also as large as life. This means that not only will you have to be passionate toward the girl—you will have to be at the very least *affectionate* toward the other men. Just as the two girls who share one man's bed may enjoy some lesbianesque byplay, so several men who make love to one girl will find themselves participating in a little homosexual petting.

Unless you already have some sexual-identity problem—in other words, unless you're suffering psychologically from homosexual tendencies—a bit of sexual sport with other men won't do you any harm at all. The perfect lover in this situation will join in without reservation. If you can't take part in an orgy wholeheartedly, there's no point in taking part in one at all.

What sort of things should you do? Well, you don't have to *kiss* the other men or anything like that, if the idea doesn't appeal to you. But you could help your compadres by rubbing their penises to erection, and guiding them into whichever of the girl's orifices takes their fancy. A young writer I know developed a penchant for fellatio, even though he is not homosexual per se. "I'd always been curious about what it was like to have another man's cock in my mouth," he said. "When I had the opportunity to do it, and actually managed to get up the courage, I found it wasn't so ghastly after all, and in the end I really enjoyed it. I'd never do it alone with a man—I can only do it as part of a thing with a girl. But all I can say is that a man knows far better than a girl how another man can be aroused, and as long as I *know* deep down that I'm not homosexual, I'm quite happy about it."

The second point to remember about "gang-bang" sex is that it's not worth doing anything to the girl that any of you will regret. If she's had enough, of course it's time to cool it. Sometimes it's wiser to stop even *before* she feels she's had enough. If she's tipsy, or a little overexcited, it could be in her own interest for you to withdraw gracefully and make sure she gets home all right. Just use your head and your sense of responsibility. She may get carried away in the erotic heat of the moment, but don't let her do anything that will make her hate herself, or you, or anybody, when tomorrow's dawn comes up.

What a girl is prepared to do with several men depends very much on her mood and her personality. While some girls don't mind four or five men having sex with them in succession, they're not too keen on the idea of having two men inside them at once. If the girl you're screwing is excited by the idea of simultaneous vaginal and anal sex, however, there's a way of doing it that allows all of you maximum comfort.

One man should lie on his back on the bed. The girl should then lie on *her* back on top of him. He should liberally lubricate his erection and insert it in her anus, as far as he possible can without hurting her. The second man should then lie face down on the girl, supporting himself on his hands and feet, and slide his penis into her vagina. The man underneath should hold the girl, since the force of two penises pumping in and out of her at once is considerable.

While all this is going on, I'd remind you that a third man could be accommodated in the girl's mouth. The real trick is to see if all four of you can then have a simultaneous orgasm.

One of the few firsthand descriptions of multiple sex I've seen appears in Edward Thorne's book of interviews, *Your Erotic Fantasies.** The girl talking is a twenty-two-year-old secretary.

"James and David and I all got drunk. Then I was back in James's bed again, and I only had my slip on. I thought, well at least I've still got my pants on,

* Ballantine Books, New York, 1973.

but I reached down to feel and I hadn't. James was lying next to me, and he didn't have anything on either, he was completely naked, and he's incredibly hairy. Then I felt someone's arms around me from the back and it was David, they were both in bed with me. David pulled my slip off and undid my bra. I was quite obliging about putting my arms up for him.

"James kissed me. He was very bristly, which I liked. I can remember thinking how nice it was to be kissed by a bristly man. I think I licked his bristles with my tongue. And David was kissing my shoulders and my neck, he felt much smoother. They were touching me between the legs, both of them, and then I felt them both pressing against me, their whatsits, penises. I was lying on my side. James moved up very close to me and got into me, and then I felt David pressing at the back, and he got into me at the back, and I couldn't believe the way it felt. I just felt full of men.

"David was hurting me in the back, but when he slipped out I couldn't wait for him to get back again, I wanted them both in me, both at once, and they were rubbing against each other inside me, they said they could feel each other in there, and David had a climax at the same time I did, and James had one just after, and we lay there in a sweaty heap."

Your girl, and your orgy, may or may not be as enjoyable as this one. All I can say is that you, as a perfect lover, should do everything you can to make sure that one and all have a more than ecstatic time.

In the words of the Musketeers: "All for one, and one for all." Or in yet another classic saying: "That's what friends are for."

THIRTEEN:
The Kink and I

When I was a Boy Scout, I came last in my troop in the knot-tying contest, which is undoubtedly why I haven't become a bondage fetishist. It's very hard to be a bondage fetishist if the girls you tie up can get themselves loose without the slightest difficulty.

But what *about* bondage, and leather, and rubber, and whips? Where does the perfect lover, in all his perfection, stand in regard to these?

If you're trained to be a soldier, you're trained to keep physically fit for combat and you're trained to fire a gun, even though you might end up as an electrician in a barracks, soldering fuses together. Similarly, a well-trained lover knows everything there is to know about sexual variations, even though he may never actually try them out.

Unless you are actually a sex fetishist—which means that you depend completely for your sexual satisfaction on being tied up, or being dressed in rubber, or something of the kind—kinky sex will simply be a way of acting out some harmless but stimulating erotic games.

Weird sex variations, however, are *not* something that a perfect lover tries out on a first or second date. If you have it in mind to try out something rather peculiar, he heh, the girl must *trust* you first. I know you don't *look* like a maniac, but then even maniacs don't look like maniacs, and not many girls are going to feel comfortable about a perfect stranger, even if he's a perfect lover, binding them to the bedpost with rubber hose and whipping them with a Sam Browne.

If it's bondage you have in mind, choose a fun moment with a girl you've known for some time; then tie her ankles to the end of the bed, with her legs wide apart, and tie her wrists together in front of her. Use neckties or cloth belts—cords and ropes can be very painful.

An absolutely dead serious and unequivocal word of warning: *never* tie anything around a girl's neck, *never* suspend her from anywhere by ropes or bonds, *never* gag her. Strangulation and suffocation happen tragically quickly, and police files are absolutely crammed with death reports connected with bondage.

Back to the fun, though. When your girl is safely tied up like Harry Houdini on an off-night, the idea is to ravish her, titillate her, arouse her to the screaming point by any means, fair or foul. Use a vibrator on her clitoris and up her vagina as she lies there helpless. Give her a powerful dose of your finest and most stimulating cunnilingus. Have intercourse with her, and then stop having intercourse with her, so that she pleads with you to continue. In other words, enjoy yourself, and make sure you do, because the next part of the bondage game is that she ties *you* up, and she can do anything she wants with *you.*

Exercise Fifteen:

Buy yourself a Scout handbook and teach yourself a few basic knots. Practice by tying your own ankle to the end of the bed. Keep on practicing until you can tie the knots quickly and smoothly. There is nothing more likely to put a girl off bondage than waiting for half an hour while you fumble with a huge Gordian knot made of hundreds of grannies.

Bondage is pure fantasy stuff, so camp it up a bit while you're doing it. Be threatening and fierce, and make out you've got rape on your mind (which you have, except she'll be willing). The fun of it is that she should feel completely helpless in the face of your bizarre tastes and predilections.

Sex aids can also add a touch of kinkiness to your sexual relationships. Most of them are ridiculous and next to useless, but the *idea* of them is usually erotic, and for a one-time-only thrill, it's worth bringing a box of them to bed.

The standard sex aid is the plastic penis-shaped vibrator. They cost from $2 to $15 and can give you a little extra buzz of excitement during love-play. A favorite trick is to insert a vibrator into a girl's backside while you insert your cock in the front—an arrangement that gives both of you an added hum of sexual sensation.

Close cousins to this vibrator are the so-called Angels Delight, an egg-shaped plastic vibrator for girls, and a vibrating device which a man can strap to the back of his hand, thus transmitting a tingling sensation to her clitoris through his own fingers.

Dildoes, or artificial penises, come in all shapes, sizes, and varieties. You can buy pink dildoes or black dildoes, dildoes with attached testicles that squirt out simulated sperm, dildoes that strap on to men, dildoes that strap on to women, double-ended dildoes, dildoes with vibrators inside, six-inch dildoes, ten-inch dildoes, foot-long dildoes. You want a dildo, they got dildoes. Prices around $15–20.

Not many dildoes are bought by lesbians. According to the sex-aid companies, most are bought by married men for use on their wives. In fact, they're quite a useful tool to have around if you suffer from premature ejaculation, or if your girl friend or wife takes a long time to come. Fido may flop, but your trusty dildo will remain stiff and buoyant, even after it's shot its surrogate wad.

Jokey condoms are another kinky thing to try. You can get black ones, speckled ones, ones with knobs and fins and flaps and spines and God-knows-what on them. One woman said it was like being fucked by a randy sea anemone! But be careful: few of the "special" sheaths are true contraceptives, and you will need other protection.

French ticklers, which are like tiny bits of rubber bathmat attached to the base of your cock with a ring, are in my opinion, an absolute washout. They are supposed to rub the girl's clitoris as you make love to her, but girls either feel nothing at all or they complain of being scratched or rubbed too hard. Don't waste your money.

A centuries-old device which has only recently found its way on to the mass sex-aid market are Siamese love beads. These are a string of six or seven rubber "peas" which are pushed up the anus prior to lovemaking. At the moment of orgasm, they are pulled out, one by one. The sensation, to say the least, is peculiar.

While we're on the subject of rectal sex, here's another small warning. Don't push anything up the ass that you can't get out again. Always hold vibrators, if you insert them into the anus. Doctors have told me time and time again that vibrators have an unfortunate habit of getting lost up people's rectums, and their removal can necessitate a major (and nasty) operation.

There's a (true) medical case history of five Viennese

students who, for a joke, pushed a frozen pig's tail up a prostitute's anus. When the heat of her rectum melted the ice on the tail, the spiny hairs on the tail opened out, and the students found it impossible to remove it. Only the ingenuity of a local doctor, who slid a lubricated glass cylinder *around* the tail, was able to save the girl from difficult and painful surgery.

So, you know, go easy with the pig's tails.

Unless your girl friend is a giantess, however, there is no immediate danger of your losing your cock up there. Many men and women have an aversion to the idea of anal intercourse because the bottom is traditionally a dirty place. But actually, there is rarely any fecal matter at all in the rectum, except when you're actually crapping, and so, provided you take certain, well-trained precautions, you should find it an exciting and enjoyable variation.

These are the precautions: make sure your girl friend has washed herself thoroughly before anal sex; make sure you lubricate your penis with Vaseline or KY before attempting insertion; make sure you do not continue with anal sex if it is causing her continuous pain; and *always* make sure that you wash your penis before inserting it into her vagina again. Got it?

If you reach around and stimulate your girl friend's clitoris during anal sex, you should be able to bring her to orgasm quite quickly, even though the tighter muscles of her bottom do not allow very much movement of the penis.

What about peeing? Lots of girls feel like wetting themselves, and sometimes do, when they have an orgasm. This is nothing unnatural. Something a little more way-out is this business of urinating over each other, even to the point of peeing into each other's mouths. In homosexual slang, this is called "the golden shower."

If I'd written this book a few years ago, I probably would have ignored this taste for urination—urolagnia, as it's called. But I have received so many letters about it from readers of *Forum* and *Private* magazines that I believe the *desire* to practice urolagnia, if not the practice itself, is more widespread than most books on sex would suggest.

In large part, it is connected with the semi-sexual pleasure of releasing urine after holding it back for a long time. But there is also a great deal of *humiliation* involved, particularly when men sit in the bath and ask their wives or girl friends to pee over their faces, and vice versa.

If you feel like doing it with your wife or girl friend, then by all means do it. As long as you observe your training as a perfect lover—in that you do it because you *both* enjoy it—I can't see any particular harm in it. Drinking urine in large quantities is not recommended, but then I feel the same about Swedish beer. Just make sure you have a good shampoo afterward.

Now what's this about rubber and leather and silk? Unless you're really determined to try out some of the true fetishist outfits, I don't really recommend your getting very deeply into this field, for the simple reason of expense. A full rubber outfit for the dedicated rubber-fiend may cost $300–400, including lace-up head mask with inflatable gag, lace-up straitjacket, pants with tight-lacing for the penis, and other little extras.

Again, the main emotional motivation for rubber fetishism appears to be a desire for *humiliation*. A lot of psychiatrists have claimed that a sexual attachment to rubber must be connected with bedwetting and rubber sheets back in the fetishist's childhood, but then why doesn't everybody who ever had a rubber sheet suffer from it? (Or enjoy it, as the case may be?)

Since I think it is important for a perfect lover to understand his own secret sexual kinks and desires, I went and talked to the woman who must be the world's leading expert on subjugation and humiliation in sex—Monique von Cleef.

Monique is a blond, big-busted lady of fifty who runs what she calls a "sado-therapy" service in her house at Cornelius Houtmanstraat 2a, in The Hague. Telephone, for those of you interested, is: 070-856392.

Up to two hundred clients come to Monique to be sexually humiliated. She binds them up with ropes, hangs them by their heels from the ceiling, and gives them enemas big enough to float the Ark. She makes them crouch in playpens wearing diapers, and sit on three-legged stools with seven-inch wooden dildoes sticking up from the seats. She puts spiked "muzzles" on the ends of their penises and hangs lead weights from their balls. Anything that's anywhere in the humiliation line, Monique provides.

"I can humiliate any man who comes to me," smiles the sado-therapist. "I can make him so small that I can break him down completely. I am not doing this because it is my own sadistic scene, but because I know what he wants, that I must control the situation all the time.

"Most of the men who come to me are important businessmen in their own right, yet somehow they feel they do not deserve their authority over others. They feel a need to be told what to do themselves, to shrug off all their responsibility and become nothing but slaves.

"I can have two or three slaves at a time and put them

in different situations, so letting the others know what might happen to them next. I like to use a female slave, to have her together with male slaves, and then I humiliate them all in one way or another. It's not that I let the male slaves fuck the female slaves, we avoid a straight scene. We let the girl stay in the room, or hang, having clips on her nipples, and then we let the male suffer, for this is what is going to happen to him afterward. Slaves must have a real fear—otherwise they wouldn't be slaves."

Monique von Cleef is a little on the extreme side for most of us—but her bizarre sado-therapeutic setup shouldn't be dismissed too lightly, particularly if you're training to understand your own sexual emotions. If either you or your bedmate feel at times like a spot of kinky sex, you could well be expressing that little bit of sadist or masochist that most of us have lurking in our subconscious.

Unless it becomes an obsession, it's just something to be enjoyed.

You and your girl friend can base an endless variety of erotic games on the variations I've just mentioned. A friend of mine, a lawyer, very dignified in day-to-day life, once admitted to me that a favorite sexual charade of his was to pretend that he was a slave, and that his wife was the imperious Sultana of some remote Arabian state. He would crawl naked into the bedroom, where she sat on a heap of cushions eating Turkish Delight, and submit to a mild whipping from her dressing-gown cord before being "forced" to make love to her.

There are so many different sexual predilections that it is impossible to list them all here, but most of us have fairly distinct erotic preferences. These can range from a liking for a certain type of female figure (boyish, for instance) to unusual underwear (stockings, suspenders, and whatnot) to something quite extreme (like the man who wrote to me and said that he ejaculated every time he saw the fat wobbling thighs of the woman next door).

Girls have strong sexual leanings as well, and the perfect lover is just as conscious of these as he is of his own. Very few girls like over-muscular men; very few girls like extremely hairy men. Some girls go for the hard, abrupt and cynical type, while others prefer the softer, more studious personality. A lot of girls, inexplicably, get turned on by football players' legs.

You will usually find that your bedmate has one or two little kinks that you can *very occasionally* play on. One girl I knew liked to have her nipples actually *bitten* quite hard when she was reaching a climax. Another used to revel in having her back scratched. A third enjoyed a stiff finger being pushed relentlessly up her bottom.

All of these girlish preferences have a sado-masochistic feel about them, yet none of the girls was anything near to what a doctor would define as a true sadist or masochist. So don't be concerned if you find yourself enjoying a sexual variation that's mildly on the painful side, or if your girl friend starts asking you to dig your fingernails into her. The perfect lover understands that kinkiness is all part and parcel of being an erotic human being.

So send away for your vibrator, and long live the kink.

FOURTEEN:

Darling, I Am Growing Old . . .

You can tell you're growing old. Not because policemen look ridiculously young, but because you start calling women of thirty, "girls."

The principal sexual difference between men and women, as far as age is concerned, is that men mature and women decay. That's why, at the age of forty, a rugged, wise, and handsome man, with just a few becoming streaks of gray at his temples, suddenly discovers that the girls who were once his contemporaries have crow's-feet, sagging breasts, and incipient varicose veins.

Is it any wonder that his eyes begin to look backward, angel, to just-ripened nymphets in their late teens and early twenties? No, it is not any wonder. (And it is just as well, because it leaves the forty-year-old woman free to dally with just-ripened young men.)

By the age of forty, a man is more likely to have attained the state of perfect lovership, through both training and experience. But nonetheless, it isn't easy for an older man to run a satisfying affair with a girl twenty years his junior, and there are a lot of important points he should watch out for.

Point number one has got to be this. If you're a gentleman of forty, and you're embarking on a sexual liaison with a twenty-year-old girl, have you got the physical and emotional stamina to take it? Certainly, you have other things in your favor. You have sagacity and experience. You have a considerably higher income than most of her male contemporaries.

But what you don't have is youth, and there will be times, both out of bed and in it, when nothing at all will make up for that long-lost asset. You may find yourself helplessly embarrassed in front of a teen queen who hasn't got the compassion to let you down lightly.

But I know you still want to go ahead with it, because maybe this will be the last great affair you'll ever have, and next year you'll be forty-one, and five years after that you'll be homing in on your half-century. So here's some gentle advice from one who has seen some very sincere and worthy middle-aged men take some humiliating nosedives in the face of the younger generation.

Don't ever mentally detach yourself from "youth." They're just people like you, and they're not particularly different. Some of the things they say and do and like might seem alien and strange (but then you ought to see what the Swedes get up to, and everybody still accepts *them* as people).

Don't ever say: "When I was your age . . ." Don't ever say: "I don't know what you young people see in . . ." Don't ever say: "Bit before your time, I expect . . ."

As you probably remember from your own twenties, the object of most scorn was a middle-aged man trying too hard to be "trendy." Dress fashionably and well, but dress your age. Drive a car that's appropriate to your position in life, without being over-sporty (the sad thing about most of the really expensive Italian two-seaters, like the Lamborghini Countach and the Ferrari Boxer Berlinetta, is that most of the people who can afford them are too old to drive them). Develop some likes and dislikes in pop music, but don't embrace it all regardless, or reject it all out of hand. Never try and use contemporary teen slang. Know what it means, but never use it. I can remember seeing a nineteen-year-old girl actually *cringe* as her thirty-eight-year-old escort said: "I think I'm rather *with-it* now, don't you, ha ha?"

Treat your junior lover-ette the same way as you would any older woman. She will respond to it gracefully, provided you don't *always* expect her to be full of dignity and maturity. There will be plenty of times when she wants to do daffy things, like run along the beach at midnight, or steal a souvenir from an expensive restaurant. At those times don't be over-enthusiastic and don't be stuffy. Just keep your cool. And don't come out with stories of what you used to do when you were young. They will only date you.

Seduction-wise, you are at a tremendous advantage. It is important not to blow it. A younger girl will expect you to know all about love and lovemaking (although as Alan Brien once remarked: "When you've *made* love, what does it look like?"). She will expect you to take her in your experienced arms and show her everything that sex has to offer. One of the reasons she's attracted to you is that you look as though you know what it's all about.

By Christ, make sure you do. Memorize this book parrot-fashion if necessary. Then the only problem that will stand between you and teen-age blissville will be the down-to-earth question of your good old sexual stamina.

If you've been eating and exercising according to the

patterns laid down in this book, you should be in much better condition to face the rigors of youthful eroticism than your average everyday cigar-smoking deskbound businessman.

Nonetheless, you know and I know that a man reaches his sexual peak around the age of twenty-five, and twenty-five was . . . um . . . fifteen years ago. A decade and a half has passed since the years of maximum erection, and something has to make up for the inevitable fade in performance. The answer, in a nutshell, is technique.

When you take her out, don't stay out too late and don't eat too heavily. If you're feeling at all tired, take a couple of benzedrine tablets or drink a couple of cups of very strong black coffee. Don't spend hours talking or listening to records or drinking before you go to bed. I know it sounds as though I'm treating you as a geriatric patient, but the more strength you have in reserve by the time you get her between the sheets, or on the living room rug, or up against the wall in the hall, then the better you'll be.

Take the sexual initiative with her, and take it quickly. Make sure you know how to get her out of her fashionable clothes with promptness and efficiency. Bite your tongue if you're about to say: "Girls didn't wear these when I—"

Undress yourself swiftly (you weren't wearing suspenders, were you?) and join her in bed. Lie on your back, so that she will have to prop herself on her elbows to kiss you and talk to you. This will not only save you a little more energy, it will also gently direct the way things go when you actually start fucking . . . and it will direct them to your advantage. You cunning old rogue, you.

When you are lying on your back, it is easier and more natural for the girl to manipulate your penis than it is for *you* to do all the work on *her*. Subtly, the onus for successful foreplay rests on her, and most girls will plunge into it without realizing they've been gently guided.

While she caresses and possibly sucks your penis, you can be doling out nonstrenuous kisses to the face and hair, fondling her breasts, and running your experienced hands over her delightful little kewpie-doll corpus. Amount of energy consumed by this activity: about 56 calories. That means you've turned her on and only burned up the equivalent of one slice of melba toast.

Since you've started your sexual activity lying on your back, that's all the more reason for carrying on in the same position. Being on top is very hard on the elbows and knees—particularly, if you're a sedentary worker, the knees—and there's no point in wasting strength just keeping yourself up when there's plenty of other work to be done.

Actually, girl-on-top is an excellent position. As we've seen before, it enables the girl to exercise some control over the way in which she's being stimulated by your penis (if she sits up, it drives straight in; if she leans forward, it slides out), but it doesn't completely rob the man of any opportunity to direct the pace of things. If the man wants to slow down the speed of lovemaking, all he has to do is lie still himself and check his rider's movements by holding her hips; if he wants to speed it up, he can make rapid upward thrusts from the bed.

The girl-on-top position is not restricting either. You can both move easily into a side-by-side or scissors position if you want variety, or with one powerful roll, you can get on top of her without even taking your cock out.

When you're actually screwing, don't let it drag on too long, because you will find yourself being gradually sapped of strength, and by the time you reach your climax, you won't have the capacity to enjoy it to the full.

Whatever positions you choose, make sure that your penis is getting as much friction as possible from her vagina. Since she's a younger girl, she's bound to be a little tighter, so this shouldn't be difficult. Use that friction to bring both of you to a satisfactory climax well within ten or fifteen minutes. Any longer than that and your stamina will start to be impaired, and when that happens, you are in danger of losing your erection. Flopping out halfway through is bad enough when your bedmate is the same age as you, but if it happens when you're shacking up with a girl twenty years your junior—well, you can appreciate the unsaid implications that tend to follow. I'm not trying to suggest that you're an old man, but just remember when *you* were twenty, how old people of forty appeared to you then. That's what you seem like to her.

What happens if she wants more and you just don't feel you can make it? Answer: Don't worry about it. She won't have met many men, even twenty-year-olds, who can go on and on and on. If you keep the first fuck well under control, and make sure you *both* are well satisfied, then the problem shouldn't seriously arise.

Affairs between people of widely differing ages rarely last. That's something you'll have to face from the beginning. There are some notable and admirable exceptions, where an age gap hasn't affected a meeting of personalities. And when you're talking about long-term affairs, sexual technique is only an ounce of baking powder in the cake of compatibility.

But little girls grow bigger every day, and they change drastically in temperament and personality between the ages of nineteen and twenty-five. Where once they sought the security and dignity and status of going out with an older man, they begin to look for men who can more closely understand their everyday likes and dislikes, and share their discovery of life along with them. In other words, they begin to want someone of their own age and life-style.

When you sense this happening, there's only one thing to do, no matter how much it hurts. Make a dated and sentimental gesture, like George Sanders playing *The Saint,* and send her a bunch of flowers with the message: "It was beautiful, but it was not to be," and go whistling off toward a new adventure. Twenty years ago, a lot of little girls were born, and there are thousands more around.

Is there anything you can do, as you grow older, to maintain your sexual condition? In the chapter on food, I mentioned the great variety of pills and drugs and vitamins that are on sale, all of which purport to assist the maintenance of male virility. From chemical tests, these generally appear to be nothing more than overpriced and ineffective sweets.

But there are tonics widely available which are medically recognized to be of some help for tiredness and nervous exhaustion, and these, if taken consistently, could at least keep you in the right physical condition to be able to produce and keep an erection. Consult your doctor if you're feeling at all run-down, and he should be able to recommend something.

The most important point about any temporary impotence or sexual failure, however, is that it needs immediate attention. It's nothing to be ashamed about, since almost every man at one time in his life has suffered from it. As I've said before, admit it openly to your wife and girl friend, be relaxed about it, and if it still doesn't improve, then go and see someone who can help you.

Dr. Thomas Main, medical director of the Canel Hospital in Richmond, England, says that the situation only really gets serious when lovers try to conceal their impotence from their bedmates by elaborate deceptions and lies.

There's the man who comes home from the office with a bulging briefcase, so that he can pretend he's "too tired" to make love when bedtime comes. There's the man who goes to bed before his wife and pretends to be asleep when she arrives. There are even men, says Dr. Main, who pretend that their moral principles are so high they wouldn't really enjoy sex.

And there are men like the fifty-year-old husband who believe that every time they make love, it takes a month off their life. "Age," says Dr. Main, "does not stop those who want to make love." He added that potency does "come and go" and that few middle-aged people were happy about their sex life. "But any man who is happy with his sexual equipment ought to be stuffed and preserved in a museum."

Dr. Main is convinced that once a man seeks help for his impotence, and is able to overcome it, his whole life—not just his sexual life—can radically improve. He cites the case of the football player who, having conquered his sexual problems, was rapidly promoted from the reserves to the first team. "The sexually happy man gets a better job, more money, and a better house—he enjoys life as a whole."

There are several sexual aids for men who really do find it impossible to get or sustain an erection. Beate Uhse, the German sex-aid matriarch, has more or less a full selection in her catalogue. If you're interested, you can write for one to Versandhaus Beate Uhse, 239 Flensburg, Gutenbergstrasse, 12, Germany.

These aids include everything from inflatable "props" for the penis to "pubic rings" which partially restrict the blood flow from the erection—so that once the blood has filled the spongy tissues of your cock, it finds it more difficult to drain out again. There are also full-size dildoes which fit completely over your penis and allow at least a simulation of real lovemaking. Some of these are equipped with vibrators to make them buzz stimulatingly, and an "ejaculation mechanism" to spurt out special fluids whenever desired.

In my opinion, however, these aids should only be used after a doctor has made it quite clear to you that you will always have trouble with impotence. They should not be used if there is the slightest chance of keeping up a good sex life without them, because they can so easily become sexual crutches, and once you have begun to depend on them, they're very difficult to shake off.

If you're an older man, although you may desire younger girls, it's more probable that most of your sexual relationships will be with women of your own age. I was actually only kidding about the sagging breasts and the crow's-feet, because older women have a special attraction all their own (as Brigitte Bardot, Elizabeth Taylor, and countless others bear witness). But the perfect middle-aged lover who wants to make perfect middle-aged love to a lovely middle-aged woman will also have special difficulties to contend with.

Some women of forty become insatiably hungry and full of highly erotic self-confidence. They're no longer shy and girlish. They know who they want to fuck, and they know how to fuck him when they've got him. But there are thousands more who, for various reasons, have pushed the whole idea of sex to the back of their minds, and need gentle and complicated "bringing-out."

Dr. Prudence Tunnadine, of the British Family Planning Association, puts a lot of this sexual reticence down to a woman's role as wife and mother. So closely intertwined are the production and rearing of children with a woman's sexual function that they can actually interfere, quite drastically, with her feelings about intercourse.

Dr. Tunnadine specifically mentions the women who shun sex once they have had a child, feeling inwardly that they have now been fulfilled, and the women who lose interest in sex when their children begin their own sexual relationships and get married, thinking that lovemaking is all right for the young people but "not for respectable old Mum."

"The mother can even become frigid, needing reassurance that sex is normal at her age," adds Dr. Tunnadine.

How does the perfect lover or husband attempt to overcome these problems? Here's how one man, a forty-two-year-old hydraulics engineer living in New York, surmounted his difficulties:

"Soon after I was moved from a branch office of my company to the headquarters in New York, I was given a new secretary. Her name was Jennifer, she was just a little younger than me, and very efficient and *secretarial*. My desk was always neat, my coffee was always brought on time, my appointment book was spotless.

"It suddenly occurred to me one evening as I was working late that I found Jenny rather attractive. She didn't dress particularly well, but her hair was always well groomed, she spoke very well, and she had the sort of strong, clearcut face that I've always liked.

"So when we'd finished and packed everything up, I asked her if, as a reward for working late, she's like to have dinner with me. She said she would love to, and so we went to an Italian restaurant around the corner from the office. I got to know her better that evening. She was forty, a divorcee, and had two teen-age sons, both at school. I asked her whether she had ever considered re-marriage. She said no. Quite frankly, she considered that that side of her life was over. She just wanted to have a good career, enjoy good company, and leave it at that. I can remember exactly what she said: 'When you get to my age, you can't think of yourself as a lover any more.'

"I suppose, to me, those words were something of a challenge. I said: 'You may not think of yourself like that, but I think of you like that.' It was rather brazen, I admit, and all she said in reply was: 'Then I think you're wasting your time.' But I was sure I'd started something, and I had.

"Two or three days later, I invited her out for lunch. We talked a lot again then, and I simply said to her: 'Jennifer, I find you extremely attractive. Come out with me tonight.'

"She obviously realized then that there was a strong possibility we would go to bed together that night, but I think she was still pushing it out of her mind. I picked her up at her apartment, and we had dinner and then I took her dancing at a discothèque. That was what finally triggered her off. The idea that not only did I find her attractive, I thought of her as young enough to take to a discothèque did a fantastic amount for her self-confidence. We were kissing passionately by the time the taxi got us back to her building, and there was no question about whether I was going to spend the night or not.

"All the time, I had to push her to realize that she was still young and attractive. She wanted to undress in the dark, but I wouldn't let her. I undressed her myself with the lights on. She was going to apologize for her figure, but I stopped her mouth with a kiss.

"I gave my lovemaking everything I had. I treated her like a teen-age nymphomaniac in bed. We had it face-to-face, dog-fashion, sideways ... we even rolled on to the floor at one point, and were fucking on the floor. It took her a long, long time to reach a climax, and I thought I was going to fade before she made it, but when she finally did, it was fantastic. It started as a few little spasms around my cock, and then it was like ripples, and then my whole tool was gripped and released and gripped and released as though someone was squeezing it with their hands. She was panting and hissing the whole time. It was incredible.

"I sometimes wonder what would have happened to her if she hadn't met me, if no one had ever approached her. We're practically living together now, and making love all the time. I wonder if she would have stayed completely celibate for the rest of her life."

This is a good example of how some older women need to be reminded of their sexuality before they respond. The perfect lover, trained to the nth degree in sexual manners and seduction, should be able to jog their memory quickly and efficiently with just the right blend of flattery, mastery, and directness. I'd like to point out that this technique works as effectively on wives as it does on mistresses, whether the wife is yours or someone else's. A woman can only be really good in bed if her lover is really good, so it's worth remembering that your wife's performance at bedtime is a direct reflection on *your* technique.

There are other ways of showing your wife that you still think of her as a mistress, apart from leaping on her with a bunch of irises and your cock sticking out. Take her out to dinner, and treat her the way she should be treated—as your lover. Start thinking of some of the things she does for you, like ironing your shirts and making your breakfast, as part of the way in which she is constantly expressing her love for you. Just because everyone does it, just because it's a habit, that doesn't mean to say it isn't special.

And treating his women as though they're special is what makes a perfect lover perfect.

FIFTEEN:
All Together Now . . .

Now we come to the little matter of what the Germans call *gruppensex*.

Some people enjoy group sex and others don't even want to know about it, the way some people like going on bus rides and others prefer the privacy of their own car, even if it's only a Fiat 500.

If it's one of your personal pleasures, then you should train yourself to approach it in the spirit of perfect lovership, and do it very well, and with impeccable manners and technique. Since one of the basic precepts of being a perfect lover is that you should only do things that both you and your bedmate enjoy doing, it would be unworthy of you to put your girl friend into a position where she felt she had to take part in a multiple confornication just because that would be the only way to keep you around. There's nothing wrong with a girl who doesn't want to make love to you and other men in a sexually social evening, and if you respect her at all, you'll respect her desires in that direction.

If it annoys you that she won't take part in group sex, then she's not the girl for you and that's it, period.

When a perfect lover goes to a group sex party, he goes

without any reservations about what might happen there or what he might be expected to do, or else he doesn't go at all. You can't stick to one partner all evening on occasions like these, and you can't be selective. If you can't bear the thought of getting your leg across Mrs. Schwarzheim, stay at home and watch a rerun of *Madigan* instead. It's a salutary experience.

You should do the same if you're going to feel insanely jealous when Roger Augenblick, with his potbelly and spotty behind, starts ramming himself with delirious frenzy up your best-beloved girl friend. Jealousy, in any shape or form, is a "no-no" at group sex parties.

Because most group sex evenings are organized by people who are fundamentally tired of their bed partners and are looking for a change without committing secret adultery, they tend to be pretty dreary occasions. But once in a while some pleasant, sexy, and sympathetic people can get together, and if you're that way inclined, those evenings are worth attending.

Explain to your girl friend where you want to go— *never* roll up at a group sex party without having warned her what's happening in advance—and see what she says. If she's interested, you're away. If she's not, it's Richard Widmark.

Both of you should dress up specially for the occasion. It's a group sex *party*, remember? See if you can find some Tarzan-style underpants with leopard spots on them, or something of that kind. And see if your partner can buy herself some see-through split-crotch backless legless invisible panties. You know the kind of thing I mean. While I'm on the subject, I must mention a special pair of sexy male underpants that Beate Uhse sells. They involve a kind of long yellow pointy funnel for the cock to fit into, and they make you look as though you're walking around with an ice-cream cone stuck on the end of it. She calls them Goldfinger. Neat, huh? Beate also does some pretty racy stuff for women.

Have a bath or shower, tart yourselves up, leap into your car, and arrive in a state of fruitiness and goodwill. Nice point for perfect lovers to remember: before you go into the party, give your partner a really good kiss on the doorstep. You can kiss her on the lips as well, if you like.

Once you've entered the festivities, the perfect lover remembers that he is not at an ordinary party, and different social rules have to be kept in mind. If a man is obviously boring your girl friend to death, it is bad manners at a group sex do to cruise over and rescue her, as you would have done quite naturally at a normal party. He is talking to her, however boringly, because he wants to have sex with her, and that, since she's attended the party, is his prerogative.

The usual pattern to parties like these is that they kick off with plenty of booze and very light refreshments, like Kentucky Fried Chicken and cheese dip. Be careful how much you imbibe, however, because anything in excess of two stiff whiskies can impair your amazing performance, and at any group sex party you'll be expected to produce the goods several times over.

There are two kinds of group sex parties. At some, couples wander off upstairs and have sex in private. At others, everybody is expected to peel off in the living room and make out all over the place. Aficionados strongly favor the latter type, since it is more of a geniune "group," and also there is a strong stimulus from seeing and hearing other couples making love only inches away.

Being a man of taste and discrimination, you will obviously want to have sex with the best-looking girls there, but if you find yourself attached to a plain jane, you will just have to shut your eyes and do your duty. It is what is expected of you, and when you're in Rome you have to speak Italian at the very least.

Most of these affairs develop an atmosphere of reckless sexual abandon, in which everyone is prepared to have sex with everyone else, but if you come across a girl who evidently doesn't want to make love with you, there is no point in trying to force the issue. She shouldn't be there in the first place, but don't make things worse for her by insisting.

Take your sex easily and calmly, giving yourself plenty of time to relax between bouts, and you should last the evening quite satisfactorily. Make a simple agreement with your girl friend that when either of you is ready to leave, you should both leave. Group sex is supposed to be a constructive influence in sexual relationships by permitting both partners to seek variety with the full knowledge of the other. Don't let it become destructive—no party is worth that.

When you go, don't forget to say "Thank you for letting me have you."

Afterward, when you're driving home with your girl friend, be prepared to discuss what has happened. Many books on group sex that I have read suggest that neither of you should say a word about what's gone on, because talking about sex with other partners will invite invidious comparisons. But I've never believed in keeping quiet about sex, and I think it is far better that you both talk the whole thing out of your system, instead of bottling it up and wondering forever after what it was that Manny Greene did to your girl friend to make her shriek so much. Use the experience to swap new sexual ideas, and note them down for the future. A perfect lover, although he's perfect, is always willing to learn from other people's sexual techniques, and that for him is one of the greatest advantages of having sex en masse.

Unless you're absolutely satisfied that what you're doing at a group sex party, and with whom you're doing it, it is something you don't mind anyone knowing about, take care that no bright spark is taking photographs. Even when you're mixing in the most respectable group sex circles, photographs have an embarrassing habit of circulating among people you don't want them to circulate among, and could you really afford a picture of your screwing your manager's wife turning up on the chairman's desk?

Group sex should be kept completely confidential among its particular participants, and that means that everyone, including you, should remember that even walls have ears.

Here are a couple of opinions about group sex from dedicated followers:

Klaus and Danny, from Munich, are a young German couple with a deep interest in "swinging" and all things sexual. Danny has this to say about their relationship and their exploits:

"We have been married now for four years. Before we were married we lived together. We consider that our relationship is a good one, we have fun out of life. Klaus and I can talk about things together. Not only the moral problems which most married couples speak about, but we are able to share our intimate thoughts. I have no shyness or shame in front of Klaus and I feel no need to hide anything from him.

"Sex is very important to us, but when the sex is finished there are still perhaps twelve hours to live together. Although our sex is very good, no couple can make love all day, and day after day.

"Before I met Klaus, he had had four different girl friends. With them he enjoyed a variety of sex, but found he could not speak to them. When we go to sex parties, it is to have sex with somebody else, not to search for people with whom to have an affair. We may find good friends, but the true intimacies of life are only to be shared between my husband and myself.

"We have not made love in large groups, and not very often. It is better with only one other couple who both attract us, and who find both of us exciting. We have also tried it with just another man and that excites Klaus.

"I want to show my love for Klaus with my body. I will do anything at all that is likely to please him. If he wants to play with me with a dildo, that I like very much. Klaus, he can use my body in any way he likes. My mouth, my cunt, even my bottom are always open to him. His pleasure is my pleasure."

Walter and Susanne, from New Rochelle, New York, are in their late thirties and have been participating in group sex for "upward of six years."

Walter regards it like this:

"The way you hear about orgies and group sex in the newspapers, you'd think that we were all a bunch of perverts and sodomists. This is not in any way so. Our group varies from four to as many as sixteen people, that's eight couples, and I can tell you that every one of those people is respectable, moral, and, in their own way, Godfearing.

"We take part in group sex, Susanne and I and all the

rest of the crowd, because when it comes to sex we're realists. Maybe there are some exceptional people who can stay happy living and loving with one person all their lives. Well, for us that just isn't so, and we've got the guts to recognize it. We need variety and change, and to feel the love, both physical and spiritual, of someone else, once in a while.

"I would be the first man to accept that maybe our marriages aren't as good or as strong as the marriages of some other people. But the whole truth of the matter is that we are still prepared to keep our marriages together, and we've found a way to do it. That's what group sex means to us. It means we can get a bit of extra spice into our sex lives without going through the whole unnecessary trauma of adultery, of deception, of divorce, and everything that divorce entails. I know, for an outsider, what we're doing here in New Rochelle is a little hard to swallow. But if they knew how earnestly we believe in the rightness of what we're doing, I think they'd go away thinking they'd met folks with real courage."

The opinions for and against group sex are pretty endless, and we're not involved in polemics in this book. All I can do is reiterate that the perfect lover who toddles off to a group sex session should go without any nagging doubts about what he's going to do, and should make absolutely sure that if he does feel any jealousy, it's not going to be so overwhelming that it seriously damages or destroys his existing relationship with his girl friend.

Oh, and one more thing. It's more thoughtful if you wear clean socks.

Exercise Sixteen:

Arrange a group sex party for yourself, your girl friend, and at least two other couples. Run it according to the principles in this chapter, but try and avoid serving Kentucky Fried Chicken and cheese dip.

When it's all over, try and assess what effect it has had on your relationship. If the effect has been good, organize another party. If it's been bad, take her out and buy her an intimate dinner-for-two and forget all about it.

SIXTEEN:

How to Be a Perfect Gigolo

We're so used to the idea of the kept woman that she isn't in any way remarkable. Every wife, to some degree or other, is a kept woman. And there are plenty of genuine lover-supported mistresses lolling in sexually acquired apartments all over the world.

But how does the perfect lover react to the idea of being a *kept man*, a gigolo?

Well, like anything else he does in matters of sex, he does it perfectly. There are times when a wealthy older woman will be prepared to pay for the companionship of a younger man, and even when a twenty-five-year-old career girl will happily finance a relationship in which *she* does the breadwinning and *he* does the housework.

One of the more intelligent aspects of Women's Liberation has been its questioning of the traditional woman-at-home/man-in-office setup. It can sometimes make more romantic and financial sense for the situation to be exactly the opposite. A sign of how widely acceptable this attitude is becoming was the recent memorandum sent by a major American publisher to its staff, insisting that in children's books, husbands should be seen performing such tasks as changing baby's diapers, cooking the lunch, and so on.

HOW TO BE THE PERFECT LOVER

If you're fortunate enough to come across a girl who is prepared to support a situation where she provides most of the money, there are certain rules of sexual etiquette that you'll have to observe.

Firstly, the relationship should not fundamentally alter what happens in the bedroom. There will be changes, as we'll see later, but just because they're *her* sheets, and she's paid for the dinner and the wine that have made you both feel amorous, that doesn't mean to say that she's relinquished her sexual femininity. Nor can you forget about your responsibilities as far as love-play and general turning-on are concerned. Sexual politics are a little different from sexual practices, and she won't thank you for expecting her to take the initiative all the time.

But, secondly, there will *have* to be differences in the everday attitudes you develop toward her. You will have to take on a large share of the domestic drudgery if you're living together—cleaning the apartment, making the beds, taking the washing to the launderette. What do you mean, you don't know how to iron a blouse? You'll just have to learn.

If you're not actually living together, you'll still have to defer to her wishes a little more often than you would normally. She will expect *you*, in theory, to take *her* out, even if she's footing the bill, but the choice of restaurant, theater, or discothèque will frequently be hers.

Unless she feels really embarrassed about it, don't bother with that rigmarole of having cash slipped under the table when it comes to paying the check at a restaurant. If you don't mind living off her income, you shouldn't mind her openly paying for you. And don't forget to thank her for the meal afterward.

This is Norman, a twenty-six-year-old television "extra,"

talking about his relationship with Anna, a twenty-eight-year-old secretary for a high-powered oil company in New York:

"We've been living together for five months now, and we're still sexually *infatuated* to the point that as soon as Anna gets home in the evening, I want to take off her clothes and make love to her there and then on the living room floor. She totally turns me on. I think she's extremely sexy. She has a fantastic figure, beautiful big breasts, long legs, and this long brunette hair. I can't stop myself getting turned on just thinking about her.

"During the five months we've been together, I think I've earned about four hundred dollars. That was from a part I got in a TV series. I had to sit in a restaurant and drink coffee for two days while the rest of the action went on all around me. I don't think I'm a particularly good extra, I get bored too easily and I start forgetting that I'm supposed to be a background character, talking and laughing and all the rest of it. I fell asleep in one session.

"So Anna really keeps both of us. That doesn't humiliate me, although it used to at first. You have no idea how much your life changes when you're no longer providing the money for things. If you want to go to a movie, you can't say: 'Come on, we're going to the movies.' You have to say: 'Would you like to see this movie, Anna? I kind of like the look of it.' And if she says no, you're stuck. Suddenly I realize what Women's Lib is all about, man. It's all about the power of money.

"But after a while, you kind of get used to the situation. I think the biggest change that's come over us has been sexually. I know that I don't really quite have the edge over her that I had with other girls. I always try and act dominant in bed, but it doesn't totally work. In some ways it's better, in some ways it takes some getting used to.

"Here's an example: not long ago we were lying in bed, it was around two o'clock in the morning and I'd fallen asleep. I woke up and found that Anna was sucking my cock. Sucking my cock, man, at two A.M.! So I said to her, very irritable, 'What are you doing, man?' and she didn't even take my cock out of her mouth, she just pushed me gently back and got on with it.

"Anyway, after a while I started to really enjoy it, this cocksucking, and I grew so hard I thought my valves were going to blow. And I wanted to *ball* her, man. So I tried to pull her up the bed a way, so that I could get my cock into her, but she wouldn't have anything to do with it. She wanted to suck me and that was all there was to it.

"I said: 'Anna, you're going to make me come,' and all she did was say something like 'gurgle-mmmphh.' And she just went on and on until I came, and she gulped the whole lot down her throat. Then she kissed me and gave me a little cuddle and went off to sleep.

"And do you know what I thought? I mean, that was when I really realized that she had done to me what she wanted to do. I mean, normally you think of cocksucking as something a man wants a girl to do, but this was completely the other way round. She wanted to do it, so she did it, and all I could do was act just like a girl would if a guy did the same thing to her. That worried me for a little while. I thought I'd lost my masculine dominance. But it was okay. I had lost it a little, but not enough to matter."

That's an example of how sexual attitudes can be subtly affected by the man depending financially on the girl. But as Norman realized, it doesn't make *that* much difference if the girl occasionally insists on calling the tune (or as the

Australians would say about Anna's particular technique, blowing the beef bugle).

The perfect lover who is supported by his girl friend is intelligent enough to be a little more accommodating toward her sexual demands. That may sound improbably chauvinistic, but the real facts of the matter are that almost all human relationships are affected by money and everything that money represents. The only single factor that makes most men say "Good morning" to their bosses instead of spitting contemptuously in their eyes is money. And money exerts similar pressure on sexual roles.

So, if she's paying the gas bill, let her have her way now and then. But don't, for your sake and for hers, become a completely submissive stud who only responds when he's told to. In many ways, your breadwinning girl friend will need more reassurance of her femininity than a girl who depends on you for her upkeep will need. If you stay sexually dominant, you will encourage her feeling of being a woman—and maintain *your* feeling of being a man.

A submissive man rapidly loses self-confidence in his sexual ability, and that way lies the road to anxiety, impotence, more anxiety, and even more impotence. The danger would be compounded by the presence of a strong, financially superior bedmate.

Your sexual relationship with an older man who is seeking more of a stud and an erotic status symbol than a living companion will be very much more businesslike. If you don't like the woman but you're turned on by the color of her money, then you are doing something that lies extremely close to prostitution. But, like everything else, there are good prostitutes and bad prostitutes, and if you don't mind becoming the male Cabiria of your locality, then good luck.

The perfect gigolo gives his mistress what she's paying him for. He's working on a tacit contract, and sexual contracts, like building contracts, should be fulfilled. If she pays a man to put in storm windows, she wants storm windows. If she's paying you to throw it up her every Tuesday and Thursday night, then throw it up her you must.

As her paid escort, it's your job to take her around discreetly and courteously, and never ever to show publicly that you feel any contempt toward her. You've both entered the arrangement willingly, and she deserves to get what her money is worth.

I never really understood the gigolo mentality—and I still don't completely—until I talked to a young American writer who had spent six months living with a woman old enough to be his mother.

His attempt to explain his feelings toward her went something like this:

"I met Veronica quite by accident. She was locked out of her house when I was passing, and I climbed in an upstairs window for her to let her in. She offered me a drink, and we started talking. She was interested to know I was a writer, because she belonged to one of those dreadful writers' clubs, where middle-aged ladies go to recite their own poetry and discuss hopelessly how they're ever going to get into print.

"When she knew how broke I was, she asked me whether I'd ever thought of having a sponsor. I said that sponsorship was an utterly fictitious fantasy and nobody ever did it these days. She said if I thought I could write something really good, she'd consider paying me enough to live on while I did it. I thought the whole thing was a joke at first, but she invited me around to dinner to show her some of my work and talk it over.

"The dinner was very successful. She liked what I had written and said I ought to sit down for three months and write a book. She asked me whether I would like to take a room in her house while I did it. I didn't have a girl friend or anything at the time, and I thought the idea was great. I accepted.

"The very first night I moved in, I was in the bathroom when she came in. I was stark naked, but she told me not to be embarrassed, she'd had two husbands and she'd seen a man without clothes before. As I did my teeth, she stroked my back and my hair, and then put her hand around and fondled my balls and my prick. Of course I got a hard-on. It was a bit tricky with a mouthful of toothpaste.

"She asked me to come to bed with her. She wasn't bad-looking, and I was feeling quite randy, so I went. I can remember how soft I thought her body was. She was sort of curvy and pillowy. Her cunt was very wet, and I slid right into it like jumping into a swimming pool. I fucked her really hard, like riding a horse. She dug her nails into me and made noises like a cat. Purring noises.

"The next morning, over breakfast, she was completely frank and businesslike with me. She said something about liking me very much, and expecting me to share her bed with her if I stayed. She said: 'I'm not forcing you—I can't. And I don't expect you to look down on me for buying my sex. If it's a deal, we've got to be on an equal footing.' I think that was what convinced me. She wasn't going to look down on me for selling myself, if I didn't look down on her for buying me. It was just a mutually convenient arrangement, and we lived together for as long as it suited us."

In the end the writer found a girl friend, and the gigolo relationship came to a close. "No regrets—just a simple agreement to finish. I miss her, and I think she misses me. But only in the same way that you miss any good friendship and secure surroundings."

Applying the rules of perfect lovership to a financial deal like this, the most important—and the most difficult—point to remember is *honesty*. Never tell your guardienne that you love her, if you don't. Flattery is quite permissible—in fact, it's essential. But no matter how tempting it is to make life easier by professing love, don't do it. A lie like this will destroy the basic straightforwardness of the agreement—and besides, if you say you love her, she might consider reducing your financial allowance. Why should she pay for love if she thinks she can get it for nothing?

Before you embroil yourself in such a relationship, make it quite clear what your terms are. If you want to date other girls, say so—don't do it by deceit. If you want some days and nights to yourself, make it clear which days and nights they are going to be. For your own protection, keep an account book of all the money she pays you—and if she buys you a car, get an agreement drawn up in writing by an attorney which clearly states your rights to it. Rich ladies who get jilted can be litigious.

If a condition of your "employment" is that you remain sexually faithful, consider that condition in the same light as any other clause in a contract. Should you break the terms, you can expect to be given the sack.

To some, a sexual arrangement of this kind might seem extremely cold-blooded. In many ways, it is. But we all, at different times in our lives, have different needs for sex and companionship, and a relationship like this, provided it is based on clear, mutual understanding, can be just as satisfying for those who enter it as a "love-match."

SEVENTEEN:

The Friendliness of the Long-Distance Lover

The number of women you manage to screw in the space of a week is no indication of how good a lover you are. Quite often, in fact, those men who have the most girl friends are those whose sexual talents leave something to be desired. They can never find the satisfaction they are looking for, and rather than blame themselves, they put the onus squarely on the girl and go looking for another one.

I'm not suggesting that every sexual relationship you have should be a long-term relationship. Simply that when you *do* find a girl who suits you, it's worth dallying a while and building up a more-than-intimate partnership.

As we've seen earlier in this book, particularly in the chapter on kinky variations, it isn't easy to explore the length and breadth of your erotic fantasies with someone you don't know very well. Only when you've spent some time together, getting to know each other's personalities as well as each other's physical needs, can you start exploring the inner reaches of sexual pleasure.

One of the essential talents that a perfect lover must train himself to develop is that of *sexual communication,*

167

because only through honest and deep exchanges of erotic opinion can a man and a woman really begin to get sexually acquainted. All right, you know without being told that she enjoys having her breasts fondled. But how are you supposed to find out, unless she tells you, that she gets a kick from having cold spaghetti poured over her stomach when she reaches a climax?

The body is a wonderful communicator, as any subway *frotteur* will tell you. But it can only communicate so much, and after that it's got to be a question of speech.

How do you talk dirty with a girl you've only just met? The way the perfect lover does it is to talk dirty/romantic. "The way you do that makes me shiver. I love being licked there," and so on. You don't have to be all that explicit to begin with. When you know her a little better, you can start using those real candid words that I told you about before. "They way your teeth were nipping my cock there, that just blew my mind."

Only by discussing each act of love after you've done it can you progressively build up a picture in each other's minds of your sexual tastes and quirks. I don't mean that after every screw you have to go through something like a sports commentary: ". . . and then we got to first base, and that was fantastic the way you just tickled the side of my pubic hair there, and then we got into that cunnilingus, a little tricky in the rough but once things had moistened up it was real good . . ." The discussion is part of the lovemaking, and so it should be *loving*.

How do you complain to a girl about something she's doing that is hurting or irritating you?

Don't save the complaint up until after you've made love—say it at once. Just say "Yarooch" and gently take her head away if she's biting you, or "Whooops" and press your buttocks together if she's pushing her finger up your anus. You can say "Whooops" and "Yarooch" the other way around if you like, but never say anything cutting or angry, because that will cut your lovemaking dead. It may even cut your relationship dead.

The reason you shouldn't save up all your complaints until after the climax is over is because you'll spoil the satisfied mood with what sounds like a list of gripes. "Why didn't you *tell* me," she'll say, "instead of suffering in bloody silence?" And indeed, why didn't you?

If there is some little sexual kink which you want to try out with her, wait until you know reasonably well how she will react to it, and then gradually broach it. Don't be too timid, though. Remember that *your* sexual satisfaction is as important as *hers*, and that she ought to be encouraged to make an effort on your sexual behalf now and then.

I can remember a young husband, who was dying to experiment with rectal intercourse, telling me how he tried to suggest it to his wife.

He said: "Do you know that people actually have sex by putting their cocks up their wives' bottoms?"

And she said: "Do they? That sounds revolting."

It was only much later that he discovered that she had had anal intercourse several times before with an earlier lover, and thoroughly enjoyed it. Her reaction had been entirely conditioned by the reticent way in which he had put his question. "If I'd said: 'God, I'd really love to make love to you up the ass,'" he told me, "I'm quite sure it would have happened straight away."

"Quite," I replied.

I have already touched briefly on the ways in which couples can act out their erotic fantasies. But the perfect lover knows that he can only go so far during a one-night stand, and that married couples, or couples who are going steady over a reasonably long period, can develop between them quite elaborate sex games. During this erotic play, the man and the woman can explore many urges and desires that, under normal circumstances, they might have suppressed.

Here's a selection of sex games, all guaranteed tried-and-tested by real couples, that you can add to your repertoire.

Exercise Seventeen:
Perform these erotic dramas with your favorite girl.

The Rape Game   She dresses in a thin dress, stockings and garter belt, and panties, and sits reading alone in the living room. You go out of the room and pretend you're a burglar prowling around. Take your time and build up the tension. Then enter the room, snap off the light, and assault her in the dark. Literally rip her dress off her, kiss her savagely, and make sure she fights you as hard as she can for her "virginity." Tear off her panties, open your trousers, and take her roughly wherever you find yourself, even if its rolled up in the drapes.

The Prostitute Game   She's a whore. Make a rendezvous with her one evening after work in a sleazy part of town. Make her an offer. Take her home in your car. Take her up to her room, and undress without any pleasantries. Insult her. Make her do really dirty things, because you're paying her to do dirty things. Tell her she's a lousy screw and slap down your money. Then go out and have a drink to celebrate, by yourself.

The Humbert Humbert Game   Have her shave off her pubic hair, tie her hair in gingham ribbons, wear knee-socks, and act the twelve-year-old girl. Buy her sweets and take her to see *Herbie Rides Again*. In the movies, slide your fingers into her little cotton panties and feel up her hairless pussy. Take her home in your car, take her into the children's room, and push your depraved cock into her among the teddy bears. When you've satisfied your craven lust, give her a lollipop and a copy of *Mickey Mouse Weekly*—all the best pederasts do.

The Maidservant Game This time, she's in charge, and you're the cringing inferior. She dresses up in black wet-look open-front bra, black wet-look open-front panties, garter belt, stockings, and black boots with stiletto heels. You are naked, except for a frilly little French apron. She forces you to make beds, clean the bathroom, wash the dishes, and scrub the floors. While you are scrubbing the floor, she sits astride you, and as you both roll amid the water and the suds, she grips your erection and slides it indomitably into her.

The Let's-Do-All-Those-Bizarre-Things-We've-Heard-About Game This is, in my opinion, a game that should be played by all couples at least once in their sexual lifetime. They jointly decide that all those sex things that disgust them, that make them shudder, they're actually going to spend one afternoon trying out. Just to see what makes them so exciting. The rule for this one afternoon should be no holds, and no holes, barred. Either of you should be able to do anything you like to the other. Have a few sex novelties ready for this special game—a dildo, perhaps, or some of those condoms with strange attachments on them. Beate Uhse produces a natty trio of condoms called "Cocky," "Jumbo," and "Handy"—one with's a cock's head on the end, one with an elephant's trunk, and the third with five little fingers, looking rather like an evening glove for a dwarf surgeon. If, during this one afternoon, you want to masturbate into your girl friend's face, do it. If she wants to push a dildo up your backside, let her do it. Play out all those tucked-away sexual fantasies, blow out all those erotic cobwebs. You may find something you both really enjoy doing, perverse though it seems.

The worst thing that can happen is that you will find out what these variations are really like, and can decide against them. To my mind, a special afternoon like this can be one of the most exciting and refreshing events in a couple's sex life. One pair I know have a "Let's-Do-It Game" every three months—"We're very strict about only having it then, so when it comes around, we feel a fantastic thrill. It brings back that feeling of doing something very secret and vulgar, which can give sex an incredible charge."

Apart from giving you the opportunity to try out all the fun and games, a long-term relationship does offer the chance to explore the myriad sensations that your bodies are capable of giving each other. You can begin to sense with your penis, for instance, the subtly quickening changes in her rhythm as she enters the fringes of her orgasm. You can hear just how her breathing alters when you stimulate her *here* or *there,* and how she moans when you drive yourself deeply in.

Most sexual textbooks, mainly because they run out of variations to tell you about, mention something called carrezza. Carrezza is when you insert your penis into her and you lie there *immobile* and kind of work yourselves up to a climax that way. Well, I wouldn't recommend it, not as a way of getting your rocks off, anyway. It's like going to the movies and watching the opening title for an hour and a half. What it can be good for, though, is training yourself to *twitch.*

Exercise Eighteen:

Insert your erect penis into your loved one. Resist the temptation to jiggle up and down. Stay still, hold her close. Now, using the penile responses you have so beautifully trained in Chapter Two—*twitch*. When you twitch, get her to twitch in response. Try and perform different kinds of twitch—long ones—quick ones—and get her to tell you which twitch is which.

There will be times during intercourse when you can drive your penis deep into her body and twitch it with considerable effect.

When you're involved in a sexual relationship with a woman that looks like it will last several years, or even a lifetime, the success of that relationship will depend entirely on what you, as a perfect lover, and your bedmate (as a perfect mistress or wife) put into it. As we've seen, no one is capable of being entirely consistent in sex. Sometimes you feel like it and sometimes you don't. But after several years, it is easier than you might think to get out of the habit of making love, and it will need work and effort on your part to make sure that doesn't happen.

When I first married, I imagined, idealistically, that most couples who appeared to be happily married also had a reasonable sex life. It was only when I ran into marital problems of my own, and talked at considerable length with other couples about the troubles they had experienced, that I realized, with some sense of shock, that almost all of them had quite serious sexual difficulties. Many couples, married for only six or seven years, had almost given up sex completely, and were living routine day-to-day lives without even considering the physical side of their relationship.

It reminded me of the cartoon of the run-down middle-aged couple sitting in a tenement, with the wife looking dully at the husband and saying, "It just occurred to me, Harry ... what we need is a change of pace ... that's what we need, a change of pace ... a change of pace, that's what we need ... it just occurred to me ... a change of pace ..."

Passion inevitably fades with familiarity. The first time you went to bed with your wife, you had an erection to end all erections, just because she was next to you and you were both naked. Now it takes work, and imagination, and effort to get it up. But the perfect lover takes that trouble, even when he's tired and his senses are dulled by an ordinary old day like any other. And that's when all the training he's taken from this book can overcome "familiarity fade."

Several counselors and doctors recommend that when a couple feel sexually jaded, they should take themselves away on "a second honeymoon." I am completely opposed to this idea, even though the holiday in itself might do you both good. Your long-term sex relationship has got to work in your normal milieu, not just for a brief fortnight in Spain. Almost everyone I know who has tried this way of pepping up their sex lives has found that as soon as they return home, things go back to their humdrum, unpassionate rhythm again. The feeling of doing something special to perk up your erotic appetites has got to come from within yourselves, not from romantic but temporary surroundings.

Simply *doing* it, whether it's ecstatic or not, is worthwhile. It keeps you physically closer together, and makes it much less difficult to make love when you really do feel like it.

In Sweden, with its live sex shows, one has the unusual opportunity of talking to men and girls who are professional lovers. Since their job is to have sex on the stage every day in front of hundreds of people, they know all about the stresses and strains of long-term relationships, but at the same time their experience shows that practice makes and maintains perfect lovers.

Here's twenty-eight-year-old Goran Harryson, who performs on stage with twenty-two-year-old Gunilla Mattisson: "We make love just as frequently whether we work or not. We perform at least a few times a day, but our record was at a party in southern Sweden, where we performed fifty-two times in four days—twelve on the first day, then sixteen, six and eighteen. For all of these fifty-two times, we missed—that is to say, it didn't work—on only three of them."

This is twenty-two-year-old Selka, who is married to Tony, twenty-one, and who performs with him on the stage. "The owner of a sex club and I discussed intercourse on the stage, and we decided that I should arrange a sex show. I liked Tony a lot—we went out together regularly and, well, I suppose that it was I who convinced him to begin with live shows. The decision proved to be a happy one from several points of view. Tony, you see, had previously had strong homosexual tendencies and had scarcely met a girl before me. That made him interesting for me, and he in turn found me completely fascinating. Later, this combination and our intercourse in front of the public brought us very close together. We always carry out our program successfully. But we have found that after four or five shows, Tony has got to let it go—that is, have an orgasm and spray it out. Otherwise he can't get it up again—it just isn't possible for him to get excited again and again without being allowed to reach an ejaculation. And of course the public love seeing how his load sprays all over me. As far as our private sex life is concerned, it's different but just as good. It's great to be able to take it easy and do as you yourself want. You can root and grub and just let it go."

Frank, twenty-seven, who used to perform with twenty-five-year-old Kim, sums up the attitude that every perfect lover should have of accepting both success and failure in sex: "You've got to miss now and then—you're only human, you know. And after all it does deal with emotions."

With these words in mind, you are now approaching the moment when you can emerge into the world as a full-trained perfect lover. Sexually fit, physically robust, and bursting with new erotic ideas.

Gird your loins, then, and get ready for your passing-out parade.

EIGHTEEN:
The Perfect Lover, and Friend

In the Foreword, I said that my definition of a perfect lover is a man who is confident that he can give as good as he gets. By now, if you have followed the exercises and suggestions in this book with reasonable thoroughness, you should be capable of feeling that confidence.

But there are two sides to that definition. What you *give* and what you *get*. What happens if the girl you're making love to hasn't got the first notion about sex, and thinks that babies are found under onion plants? Is it any good being a brilliant lover if you haven't got equally brilliant bedmates?

I am already preparing a companion volume to this one, *How to Be a Perfect Mistress* (and/or wife), but until you can drop that edifying book into your partner's hot little hands, here are a few basic tips on educating her into the ways of advanced sex.

First of all, don't be totally deceived by your partner's protestations that she doesn't know anything about sex, and that she really isn't very good at it. Girls think (often rightly) that men are jealous animals, and would prefer them not to be highly experienced in bed. It's the old

"Where did you learn *that*?" syndrome. So they lie a little, just to be friendly.

The only empirical test of a girl's erotic capabilities is good old-fashioned intercourse, during the heat of which it is very difficult for a girl to hide her light under a bushel, or her babies under onion plants. If she caresses you expertly, sucks you like Linda Lovelace, squirms with all the right rhythms at the right times, and comes to a satisfied climax at the end of the proceedings, then you're probably not dealing with a complete novice. You may be, but it's highly unlikely.

The beginner will follow your every lead, will expect *you* to undress her, will leave *you* to guide your erection into her vagina, will try and take *her* rhythms from *yours*, and in general will be less aggressive and confident.

Since you won't have the opportunity to sit down with her and explain everything you're going to do with the aid of colored diagrams and charts, you will have to communicate what you want her to do while you are actually making love, and mainly through body language. In other words, you will physically have to guide her until she catches on.

During love-play, a good signal is the well-known grunt of pleasure. If she does something nice to you, start grunting and purring and showing you like it. Unless she's inestimably dense, a little bulb will light up in her brain saying: "He's grunting with pleasure. I must do that some more." If she does something you actively don't like, then try and change position or move her hands or lips away.

You can use your hands during oral sex to show her the best way of stimulating you. As she sucks your cock, caress her face and lips with your fingers, and at the same time gently and almost unnoticeably guide her head into the right rhythm and the right depth of swallow.

When you've actually entered her, you may find that if she's very inexperienced she doesn't know how to move. Simply grasp the cheeks of her bottom in your hands and guide her into the correct pace of screwing, until she catches on. If she moves in a way that arouses you, apply the well-known grunt of pleasure or just say: "Mmm, that's nice." Little bulbs will go on again, and you can be assured that she won't forget that ever again.

The best way to train a girl to be a good lover is through actual demonstration; always do it clearly, always be gentle, and never lose your temper in bed. Shouting at girls because their sexual performance is rather drab is no way to make friends and influence people. The perfect lover can be a cad, but he is never a bully.

More and more girls are sexually knowledgeable these days, but there are still staggering gaps in their erotic education. That's why it's very important that, at the right time and in the right place, you should take every opportunity to talk about sex with your partner, and try and fill in any serious gaps (apart from the obvious one).

Some of the ignorance and misapprehension is harmless. I once knew a girl who thought that women ejaculated fluid at the point of orgasm, just like men. It was probably an odd hangover from the Victorian idea of women "spending copiously" (read *The Pearl*, and other filthy literature of the 1890s), but nonetheless she firmly believed it and no one had ever told her otherwise.

There are still girls who think they can't get pregnant if they have it standing up, and even girls who don't know of the existence of such a thing as an "orgasm." I remember reading one tremendously bitter and tragic letter to a

British woman's magazine, from a fifty-year-old wife who had just learned about the female climax. "I never had any idea that such a thing was possible," she wrote. "I feel I have been cheated, dreadfully cheated, out of years of pleasure."

"Evelyn Home," who for almost twenty years wrote a superb "agony column" in one of Britain's biggest-selling women's magazines, summed up the sexual ignorance of girls to me once by saying simply: "It is almost impossible to believe what some women believe about sex."

So even if you're dating a very liberated girl, don't be surprised and don't fall over laughing if she has one or two curious ideas about conjugation. Women are not the mysterious all-knowing creatures that some men believe they are when it comes to sex. Most men are better informed and have a clearer grasp of sexual essentials, even in matters like childbirth and breast-feeding. And a perfect lover, anyway, makes it his business to know his subject.

Because of their ignorance, some girls can appear to be unsympathetic to male sexual problems. They are looking to their lovers for guidance, and when something goes wrong they are immediately impatient and think the worst. This, from another agony column in the women's magazine *Viva*, is a typical example:

"For a man who is only in his mid-twenties, my husband is a total sexual failure, so I have to masturbate almost every day to relieve my desire for sex. I always masturbate with a vibrator, and I enjoy it so much that I have become addicted to using it. I used to have orgasms very easily, but now it is impossible for me to have an orgasm except when I masturbate with a vibrator. Is there something the matter with me? What can I do about this problem?—Abby."

The answer, from former porno writer Florence King, ran as follows:

"You have programmed yourself to respond to a vibrator instead of a real live cock. Cocks aren't powered by batteries but by living, feeling, and sometimes very sensitive human beings, so don't dismiss your husband as a 'total sexual failure' just because he doesn't buzz on signal and fit conveniently into your night-table drawer. By humanizing the vibrator you may be dehumanizing your husband.

"Since technology got you into this mess, see if it can get you out of it. If your husband has no objections, try using the vibrator on both of you while you are having intercourse. Gradually lessen its use as time goes on, like a gradual course of withdrawal from a drug.

"Or maybe you'd rather keep the vibrator and donate the total sexual failure to charity? Make sure you get a receipt from the Internal Revenue Service."

Remember that, while girls are just as fascinated by sex as men, it is still difficult for them to feel they can walk into a bookstore and buy a book about it. So have a couple of the better books on sex technique around, like *The Joy of Sex,* or *The Sensuous Woman.* If you think she won't be totally put off by the idea, try showing her a hard-core pornographic magazine like *Private,* where intercourse variations are depicted in big color pictures.

This is Belinda, a twenty-year-old American college student, talking about the depths of her sexual ignorance.

"I didn't even know about having a period until it actually happened and I was sent home from school. My mother explained that it happened to all grown-up girls once a month, and that it would continue until I was around fifty years old. But she never explained *why* I was having it, and I only discovered that six months later from a girl friend.

"I had very little idea of what a boy's penis really looked like. I had seen statues, of course, and I'd seen my younger brother naked when he was tiny, but that was it.

"When I was sixteen, I went to a rock club out in the woods, where a whole lot of Hell's Angels and hippies used to hang out. It was the first one I'd ever been allowed to go to. I was really dressed up nicely, with a new skirt and blouse and new tights and my hair all done. I guess I must've looked pretty out of place there, because everyone else was all in jeans and stuff like that.

"My friend Mary and I started talking to two boys. They were kind of tough-looking, and I thought they looked pretty dangerous, but they were okay. I never even knew their names. Mary started dancing with one of them and the other one asked me if I wanted to. I said it was pretty hot in there and I'd rather take a walk outside.

"It was beautiful and cool outside, and we went around to the back of the club and up into the woods a way. I was so innocent, this was just a walk in the woods to me. Suddenly the guy stopped and said: 'Okay, this'll do.'

"I said: 'What do you mean?' He said: 'This place. Nobody can see us here. It's okay to ball.' I hadn't any idea what he meant—well, I didn't until he got hold of me and started kissing me. I was frightened but he was very strong. After a bit, I kind of made myself relax, I thought he's all right, he only wants to kiss me, and that's nice. You can see how filled up with comic-book crap I was.

"Then he put his hand up my skirt. I said: 'Don't do that, what are you doing?' He said it was okay, I was beautiful. He put his finger up my pussy and started finger-fucking me. I thought it was kind of *rude*, but can you believe I really didn't know what was going on? I truly didn't.

"We lay down on the ground and he kept on doing this up my pussy with his fingers, and then he pulled my skirt right up and got on top of me. I don't remember him taking his trousers down or anything like that. I felt something big and tight in my pussy, and I suddenly realized about half of what was happening. I started struggling then but he held me down very firmly, and he shoved himself in and out, in and out, he didn't hurry, just held me down there and slowly fucked me. I didn't say a single word. I was too stunned by the whole thing. In a strange way I enjoyed it, because it did feel good, and it was so dreamlike that I didn't believe it was really me.

"When he was just about ready to come, he took himself out of me, and moved himself forward. Then he gave his cock a couple of little jerks with his hand, and shot his come all over my cheek and hair. I thought he'd pissed on me for a moment. I didn't say anything. I got up and brushed myself down and went back to the club and then I went home."

I talked to this girl myself when I was staying in Massachusetts, and no matter how hard I questioned her, the story was always the same. She simply hadn't known what was going on. So if you run into any girl whose ignorance of sex seems too enormous to be true, don't be alarmed.

HOW TO BE THE PERFECT LOVER

Either she's trying to fool you into thinking she's a pure and unsullied virgin, or she really is ignorant, and even in these days of erotic enlightenment, so-called, it's more likely to be the latter.

NINETEEN:

Diary of a Perfect Lover

All of us like to keep souvenirs of the most important events in our lives, which makes it surprising that sexual souvenirs are considered to be another example of male chauvinist piggery. Maybe they are, if they amount to nothing more than score-keeping on the number of girls you've slept with, like notches on a gunslinger's Colt, but if they're a sympathetic logbook of love, I'm all in favor of them.

Parents, after all, are proud to collect photographs of their growing children, and mark their height on the wall. Research chemists keep their notebooks as essential reminders of the development of their work, and seasoned travelers revel quietly in the number of stickers on their luggage.

So why shouldn't a man keep a detailed record of his love life, charting the growth of his sexual technique and experience? It's surprising how easy it is to forget what you've learned about sex and sexual emotion, and momentary insights that might one day stand any lover in good stead can be lost forever in the maze of memory.

Particularly while you're training yourself to be a perfect lover, it is important to keep a diary or log of everything you've done and discovered. Keep photographs of the girls you've known, and along with the photographs, try and write as clear and objective a record as you can of what you've done with her sexually. You don't have to make an entry every day—only at those times when you definitely feel you've made progress toward better love-manship, or when you realize you've made a mistake that you don't want to repeat.

One of the most extraordinary sex diaries I ever saw belongs to a university lecturer, now in his mid-thirties. Not only was every incidence of intercourse recorded in pains-taking detail in neat handwriting, but all kinds of keep-sakes were taped to the diary's pages—Polaroid snapshots of naked girl friends, locks of pubic hair, panties, and other assorted frippery. He talks about bequeathing the book to the nation when he dies. I'm not suggesting that you should keep a book of this sort, but try and make yours as comprehensive as you can. One point, though—keep the diary well locked away. Wives and girl friends will understandably fail to appreciate its importance.

During the planning and writing of this book, I asked a close friend, a thirty-two-year-old American writer living in London, to try and follow the perfect lover training program and keep a detailed account of everything that happened to him sexually over a period of three months. This is the result:

March 10: Today I had a try at all the penis exercises. I found it easy to get an erection in front of the mirror, but maybe that was because I turn myself on. It took me nearly two hours to bring myself off just by thinking about it, and then I had to read an incredibly dirty book to make myself feel horny enough, and employ a little help from Mrs. Palm and her five daughters. Having ejaculated once, I found the masturbation exercises (five times in an hour) completely impossible, but will try again tomorrow.

March 12: Masturbated three times in an hour and feel exhausted. Also gave myself a thorough overhaul—bought new clothes, new slacks and jacket, had what's left of my hair cut, cleaned teeth, and pared fingernails. Cleaned my shoes too. I turn myself on even more than ever now.

March 13: Tried the sex motivation test and found I was just above average. Strange, that. I always thought I was a sex-mad lunatic. Masturbated *four* times in an hour and had to have a drink afterward. Have also started exercising and dieting and feel like hell.

April 6: I am beginning to feel particularly healthy and fit after all this knees-bend stuff and a restricted diet. Have almost lost my protruding stomach and actually managed to run up three flights of stairs without having to have artificial respiration afterward. More important, though, I tested out the bold and confident approach to women and have picked up a very passable young bimbo. Her name is Agnes and she works in the ——— airline office. She is redheaded, with small boobs but a neat figure, and I took a liking to her straight away. I made a reservation to fly to Paris and simply said I'd like to reserve her as well, for dinner. And gave her a wide grin. She said fine, when. I could hardly believe it. So in two days' time we are going to fill our faces at Pontevecchio and also hopefully I am going to fill her.

April 9: I have not screwed Agnes yet, and fear I have not read my instructions carefully enough. It isn't easy to remember to do everything at once. If she'd said to me then: "Are you a perfect lover?" I would've said: "No, but I read the book." She is twenty-one and very cute. She comes from Scotland and her old man is a laird or something like that. She likes the movies and art galleries and is moderately intellectual, in other words she's never read any Irving Wallace. I think the mistake I made was to come on too heavy too soon. Also I have to admit that when I took her back to my place, it did look as though it was all ready for a private orgy. I'd put some girl's cleansing tissues and stuff in the bathroom and I think she thought I was already living with some bimbo and wanted her to fill in a spare night.

April 14: Training programs be praised, I have made Agnes. We spent the afternoon at the Hayward Gallery gawping at a lot of pictures, then had a *light* meal with a bottle of wine, then she asked me back to her apartment. We kissed, we cuddled, and I got her out of her clothes like a stage magician. She was wearing a dress with puffy sleeves with elasticated wrists and I remembered to remove the wrists first and then the puffy bit, and I knew all about the zipper under the armpit, and her tights slipped off like a dream. She was wearing these tiny white panties and her curly red pubic hair made a small fringe all around them. Her breasts are indeed small but have fantastic soft pink nipples like the erasers on the ends of pencils. I tried to remember to get all the love-play in, and got her on her back on her sheepskin rug in the living room and opened her legs up real wide and licked her juicy little cunt until she started shaking and shivering like a pneumonia case. I don't know whether it was anything to do with the cock exercises or not, but I had the hardest hard-on I can remember, and I lifted her ass up so she could watch as I pushed it in, big purple head into little ginger slit. She didn't exactly screw like a rattlesnake, but when it went right up her, she started writhing and bouncing like nobody's business. She was worked up all right, and was biting my shoulders and panting, but I couldn't seem to bring her to orgasm, and after a while I just had to shoot, and then I remembered I hadn't checked whether she was on the pill or not, and I went into a cold sweat about that and practically lost my hard. So not knowing what to do, I asked her right there and then, and she said yes, so I shot. But it was all messed up. It hasn't affected our *relationship*, but I think I'm worrying too much about getting everything right.

April 15: Today I tried the exercise with the ball on the piece of elastic. I thought this was a damnfool exercise when I first read it, but I have to admit it does give you a certain amount of kinky talent. Tonight I want to get Agnes to give me a blow job.

April 16: Another technique that works. I started off by licking Agnes, and then kind of casually waved my pecker in the general direction of her luscious young lips. She took the hint straight away. She was too gentle at first with her licking, and then too fierce, but the "grunt of pleasure" system got her into line quite quickly. She finished me off by rubbing me with her hand, and didn't mind at all when I shot my load all over her breasts, so maybe there's hope for the big swallow.

April 25: Despite the pleasant companionship of Agnes, I am still working hard at my perfect lover pickup technique, and want to try it in a restaurant somewhere, which I guess is the most difficult to manage. I think if I can do that, I will have a lot more confidence in my pulling ability. At the moment I am inclined to think my thing with Agnes was something of a freak.

April 29: I haven't managed the restaurant pull yet, but it's been a big day, perfect-lover wise. I have exchanged meaningful glances with a girl in a bookstore not far from my place. She is Jamaican or something, so that should prove interesting. She also has Brobdignagian boobs, between which I would much care to wallow. Also I have ass-fucked Agnes, and she certainly didn't complain as much as Maria Schneider, but I did use Vaseline instead of butter, like Marlon baby. I didn't even have to ask her.

We were lying in bed in the morning round at my place, and she was half-asleep to begin with. She had her back to me so I started putting my arms around her and fondling her breasts, and then I fondled her ass and twisted my finger up it. Then I reached over and got the lubricant out of the bedside drawer and smeared it on my cock and her ass, and opened up the cheeks of her bottom and up it went, like a disappearing trick, all the way to the balls. She was really relaxed, which helped, but then she tightened up and gripped me so hard I could hardly shift my cock at all. But I was so turned on anyway I came practically straight away. I think she enjoyed it, but I didn't stick to my lessons, and I forgot to give her enough attention, because I was so wrapped up in my own feelings. She still hasn't reached an orgasm with me and that worries me somewhat.

May 8: I have almost forgotten Agnes and her little problem because today I pulled the amazing Dolores, the West Indian bookstore girl with the knockers like zeppelins. She is only eighteen but knows where it's at. I asked her to come out dancing and we went to a discothèque. She turned up in the shortest white dress I've ever seen, and white boots, and I have to admit it gave me a kick being seen with her. She is tasty in the extreme. I made a big effort to follow the book and I have made a list of outdoor places where we could go to screw. The weather is still a little cold but I have blankets and a sheepskin coat in the car, and next time we go out together I want to give it a try, all in the cause of science.

May 10: Agnes has responded much more to my trying harder to turn her on and understand her sexually. She still hasn't climaxed, but I think the day cannot be far away. When we made love last night, I made a conscious effort not to think about me and what I was feeling, but about her and her pleasure, and even though I couldn't completely ignore myself (which I guess I shouldn't anyway) the result was far better. In the morning she sucked me off, and although she didn't actually swallow, she had come on her lips. I did what the book said and kissed her right afterward. I don't know who was more surprised, she or me. But it didn't taste of anything, so no worry.

May 15: Bookwise, two important events occurred today. I attempted to ravish the coal-black Dolores in the woods, and it didn't completely work because it was too damned chilly, and I bought myself a "panic box" for stowing telltale items in when either Agnes or Dolores call. What happened in the woods (not far from Box Hill, at nine in the evening) was that I drove Dolores up there because it was a beautiful evening, quite warm for the time of year and a beautiful sunset. And we were rapping really well, and being tremendously affectionate and turned on. I parked the car by a footpath, and I hauled out a couple of blankets and we walked up to a place I'd seen before, where a whole line of trees and bushes kind of screen you off from the road. I put the blankets down and we lay down and kissed and fondled. She was wearing a long skirt but it was a wraparound and I could get my hand in.

I got my fingers into her pants and I could feel all her tight curly hair, and she was so squelchy there was no doubt that she was turned on. But it was growing colder and colder and our teeth were chattering, and there was no question of taking our clothes off. In the end it had gotten so cold that we called it an evening. I tried to get her back to my place afterward, but she said she wanted to go home, and I wasn't in the mood for arguing.

May 23: The Dolores affair (to coin a phrase) has petered out a little, but I am keeping the home fires burning with the occasional visit to the bookstore and the once-a-week telephone call. Agnes is going great guns. I thought she was a little drippy at first, but as I grow to know her better, I realize she's quite a little swinger in her own way. I am intending to cap my three months' trial period by ravishing her in a highly dangerous place, as per the training course.

May 29: I think I have practically won my laurels as a smooth and perfect lover. I have successfully had intercourse with the wonderful Agnes during a garden party held by some dear old ladies I know in aid of some charity in Africa or other. They asked me to go along and bring a friend, and so I took Agnes. She dressed up in a beautiful summery white dress and a white hat with a pink bow, and looked fantastic. I wore my cream-colored suit and looked like the Great Gatsby on his day off. The garden was full of flowers and bushes, and after tea, Agnes and I went for a stroll in the orchard. The apple trees had just finished blossoming, the grass was knee-deep, the day was hot and sunny, and everything was terrific. I told Agnes how beautiful she looked, how much she turned me on, and everything like that, and we fell to kissing and fondling and getting pretty fruity, which is appropriate for an orchard. She stood up by a tree, and I gently lifted her dress at the back, and took down her white knickers a little way, then opened my trousers and slid myself in. Normally, you know me, I can hardly think of anything to say, but I had been working on that, and that afternoon I was whispering beautiful romantic nonsense to her. All the while she was clinging on to that apple tree, with her pretty little bum stuck out, and I was ramming my cock in and out of her with a first-class number-one erection. You could hear and even see all these old ladies strolling around, but nobody guessed what we were actually doing up against that tree. Agnes's cunt was warm and tight and fantastic, and massaged my prick until I felt my balls were going to explode. I reached around and started manipulating her clitoris and feeling it grow harder in my fingers, and she started moaning and gasping, and I was sliding my cock in and out of her ginger pubic hair, and then all of a sudden—a complete surprise—she went "Oh" and bent double like a jackknife and *came*. That was enough to set me off, and I pumped my load straight into her while she was coming, and she felt that, and it made her shake even more. We ended up staggering around in a daze, our faces all red and gasping for breath, but it was a complete knockout. She was wonderful and I almost love her.

The writer's diary doesn't stop here, even though he had promised only to keep it for three months. It goes on to record a lengthy and apparently satisfying affair with Agnes, which at the time of writing is still going strong. I am not suggesting that the training outlined in this book was all that helped him to seduce the girl he wanted—his own personality was already strong and he was certainly not physically unattractive. But I can only add the testimony of his own words: "What I needed badly was confidence with women, and training myself certainly gave me that."

TWENTY:

Now You've Got 'Em, How Do You Get Rid of 'Em?

Anything that's hard to come by, with the sole exception of money, is hard to get rid of. That includes girls. The harder you've battled for them, the more cunning and convoluted your seduction, the trickier it is to dismiss them when the loving has to stop.

After all, they've surrendered to your perfectly trained charms because they fancy you, and the more you've had to attract them the more attracted they'll be. Just as you've won them, they feel they've won you, and there you both are, caught in the lobster pot of love.

How does a perfect lover manage to dismiss his worn-out loves? The answer depends on whether he wants to get rid of them permanently, or whether he's simply temporarily tired of his current bedmate and wants to keep her in reserve for possible future use.

If you want to end an affair forever, you have to end it forever. That means you have to make it uncompromisingly clear, in four-foot neon letters if necessary, that this, baby, is THE END. This might sound brutal, but it is in the nature of women in love to live in eternal hope (viz., Eleanor of Aquitaine, who was still bananas about Henry

II after ten years in solitary confinement). That hope will transmute anything you say that's less than a total "No" into a "Maybe" or a "Possibly" or a "See you sometime."

Don't take her out for a romantic farewell dinner. The thing has to be done in cold blood. That doesn't mean, however, that a telephone call or a letter is adequate. Be bold and determined enough to see her face to face, and explain that it's over. Tell her you've enjoyed it, if you really have. Then go, and don't come back.

If she phones you in tears and desperation, stay steady and firm, and refuse to see her. It will only prolong the agony if you go around to comfort her, because the last person who can help her over her pain of parting is you. It's like giving morphine to an addict in the middle of withdrawal symptoms. The perfect lover is perfect enough to face the cold old facts of life and act accordingly.

A parting, if effected with surgical neatness, can later lead to a firm friendship. I know several divorced or separated couples who, once their wounds have been satisfactorily licked, have become close platonic buddies. After all, there must have been some kinship of spirit for an affair to start in the first place, and provided that you don't allow a break-up to drag itself through weeks of revenge and spitefulness, there are always future possibilities.

If your affair has been a little more casual, it's possible to fade a girl out of your life for a while without losing your *droit de lit* completely. This usually only works with reasonable, mature, and outgoing young ladies who are capable of living their own lives without any kind of dependence on you. Don't expect her not to have other lovers apart from you—she will. You can't hang a woman up in a closet and expect to be able to dust her off and make love to her just when you feel like it. But if you've allowed your grand passion to lapse in a kind and careful way, you should be able to ring her up now and again and arrange an evening or two of love.

A little white lie is usually the best device for prying off a barnacle without damaging the shell. You can't see her for three or four weeks because you have a massive project at work. You have to take your aged grandmother on holiday, in case she never lives to see another summer.

Call the girl from time to time just to say "Hello," but don't make any dates for at least two months. That will have been time enough for her to adjust to the idea that she's not the number one interest in your life, but that you're still fond of her. Then you can take her out and seduce her all over again.

Don't get sore, though, if she becomes as elusive to get hold of as you were with her. She has her own life to lead, and she may well find a man who, in the immortal words of Bob Dylan, is "prepared to die for her and more."

A printing executive I met in Chicago told me that he had maintained an "on-off" sexual relationship with his high-school sweetheart through years of separation, through his marriage and hers, and that at the age of thirty-seven they were still both meeting—and making love—at least three times a year.

"We're just friends, and we'll never be anything else," he said. "But we enjoy going to bed together, and so when we meet, we usually do. It doesn't mean anything much except that we like each other physically and mentally. Not enough to live together forever, but just enough to have the kind of relationship that involves lots of friendship and a little bit of sex."

Did it affect his marriage—or hers?

"Not in the slightest. I don't know whether my wife knows about it or not. I haven't told her, but I don't think I'd be ashamed to. As far as I know, her husband doesn't know either. But it's not like a secret. We never lie about it. She knows I love Sharon and I only like her, and I know she loves her husband and only likes me."

A perfect lover never really loses a girl forever, because the things they have done together are always *memorable*. That's another plus for your sexual self-confidence. Once you have trained yourself into the skills of perfect lover-ship, any girl with whom you have had sex will always be comparing other lovers to you. And unless they've been sneaking a look at this book as well, they just won't stand up to you.

When an affair is over, try and be philosophical about it. All right, she was a stupid bitch who only wanted to date you for your looks, your money, your souped-up Charger. Okay, she nagged. She was dumb and frigid and didn't appreciate the finer points of your subtle and sophisticated personality. But you're not firing a horizontal borer who's been slacking on the production line. Resist the temptation to list her faults and smear everything in her face. It won't make you feel any better, and it will possibly give you the reputation for being a bad-tempered and unreasonable shit. So your pride's been hurt? Have some pride in your own self-restraint instead.

After you've left for the last time, make a point of sending a short note or some flowers. Something like "Thank you for everything." Don't send back any personal things she's given you, like rings or books or ID bracelets, but do make a point of sending back any property of hers that may still be lying around your apartment. Some girls are too proud to ask for their record albums or even their clothes once they've split up, and since none of us is made of money, it's only civilized to give back any stuff that's hers.

When it's all over, go out and buy yourself a quart of Scotch, put your feet up, and spend a relaxing evening listening to classical music on your stereo. It's good for the soul, and you deserve it.

Tomorrow, remember, is another lay.

TWENTY-ONE:

Now You're Perfect, Stay Perfect (and Other Sexy Thoughts)

Congratulations, you're a perfect lover. You have acquired skills that you will never forget. You have become one of the elite brethren of talented and confident cocksmen whose abilities with girls stand head, shoulders, and penis above all others. No matter how old you are, you will always be able to attract more women more often.

But now you've achieved the blessed state of perfect lovership, don't think for a moment that you can rest on your bedsprings. Your skill is part cerebral, part emotional, and part athletic, and all three of those aspects of your capability need regular exercise to keep them in shape. Your libido and your cock can grow just as flabby through lack of daily use as any other part of you.

Exercise Nineteen:
Remember that an orgasm a day keeps impotence away. Every single day, make sure that, one way or another, you reach a sexual climax. Even when you don't feel like it, even when *she* doesn't feel like it, even when your cock doesn't feel like it. It keeps you in trim, it keeps your or-

gans operating, and it reminds you mentally every single day that you're a virile male who is capable of erection and ejaculation—and that counts for a large dose of self-confidence on its own. It also keeps you in the habit of having sex—which is a habit that, once lost, takes hard work to reacquire.

Keep your seducing talents in the same sharpened condition. You may have settled down cozily with the woman you intend to stay with for the rest of your life. Your kids may be playing baseball on the lawn, your double garage may be full of Chevrolets, but that doesn't mean your existence as a sexually attractive male comes to a full stop. It's only just beginning. Your sex life will wilt only if you don't take the trouble to *seduce* any more—whether it's your wife alone, or a whole horde of different bedmates.

Exercise Twenty:
If you've been married for several years, go home tonight and seduce your wife. But don't leave it at that. Go home tomorrow night and seduce her again. And every time you feel like making love, pull all the stops out and really make her feel like the mistress she is. Who knows, in a month or two she may stop putting rollers in her hair at night.

Be sexually aware, and keep up to date with the enormous amount of sexual news and information that is available today. *Playboy* has a regular section in which it reports the latest discoveries and arguments on the erotic front, and there are several digest-sized magazines which are devoted entirely to sex discussion, like *Forum*. I don't mean you have to spend your whole life reading dirty books (although you can if you like), but it's important to your knowledge of your subject to keep yourself informed. Amateur boatbuilders read *Amateur Boatbuilder* every month, after all, and nobody thinks any the worse of them, except maybe professional boatbuilders.

When you read or think of something new sexually, do it, you may like it. The worst thing that you can do is to become sexually conservative, even on the Elysian level you have attained to date. If you are thirty years old, you've got up to 126,000 nights of love left to you. Are you going to fuck the same way 126,000 times?

To end up with, here is a checklist of forty erotic things you could to today to put that extra dollop of icing on your graduation as a perfect lover:

* Make love to her while she's dressed and you're naked.
* Make love to her standing up in the shower.
* Draw decorations on her naked body with a felt-tip pen.
* Buy her some sexy underwear, and parade it for her.
* Buy yourself some sexy underwear, and parade it for her.
* Tell her she's the sexiest thing that ever happened.
* Take a vibrator to bed, and use it on both of you, all over.
* Take two vibrators to bed, and use them both on her.
* Wake her up in the middle of the night, and make love to her.
* Eat dinner in the nude (at home, preferably).
* Take her out for a ride in the car, stop at a lonely spot, and get into some heavy petting.
* Buy a pornographic magazine and read it together in bed.
* Massage her breasts with oil.
* Have her massage your penis with oil.

* Bring her to orgasm with your tongue, without letting her touch you.
* Play hide-and-seek, in the nude.
* Shave off her pubic hair.
* Shave yours off.
* Take Polaroid photographs of each other in sexy poses.
* Lick her all over.
* Have her lick you all over.
* Make love in the garden, under a rug (or on the balcony, if you live in an apartment).
* Come home from work at midday, and make love to her.
* Pour honey on her pussy, and lick it off.
* See how many times you can make love in one hour.
* Masturbate in front of her.
* Have her masturbate in front of you.
* Masturbate together, and see who comes first (a prize to the winner).
* See how long you can make one act of intercourse last before reaching a climax.
* Ask her to think of the sexiest thing she can imagine, and then do it to her.
* Make love right in front of the stereo speakers, with a rock record at full blast.
* Make love in total darkness, without saying a word.
* Take her to the movies, and insist she wears no panties—then fondle her to a climax in the back row.
* Make love to her anally.
* Bring home a friend, and make love to her together.
* Have her bring a friend home, and make love to them both.

HOW TO BE THE PERFECT LOVER

* Smother yourselves in scented oil, and make love like slippery seals.
* Take her to a strange motel, and seduce her.
* Buy her an all-electric dildo.
* Give her a real, live cock.

That's it, perfect lover. Only 125,960 nights to go.